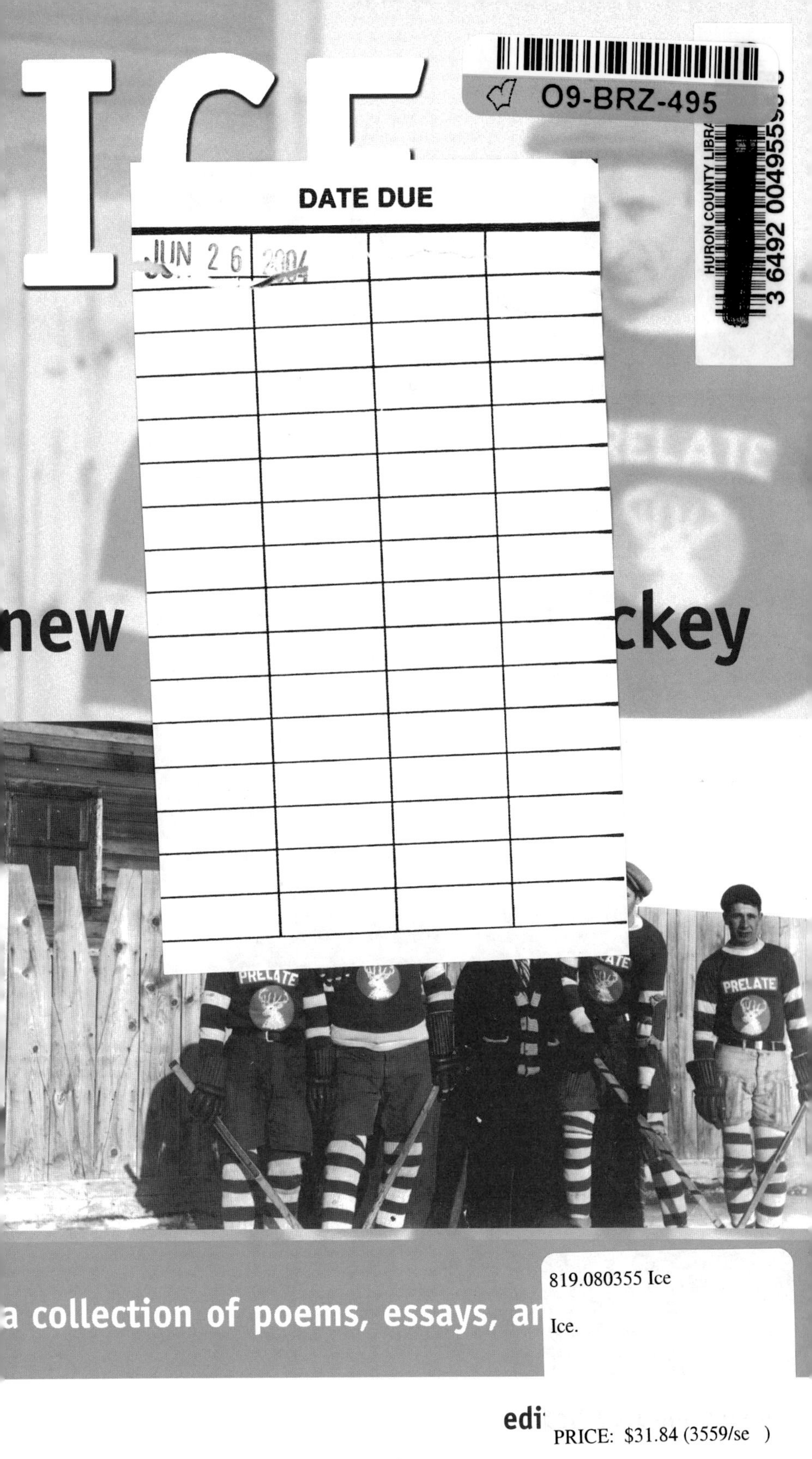

ICE
new
ckey
a collection of poems, essays, an
edi

Spotted Cow Press Ltd.
4216-121 St.
Edmonton, Alberta, Canada T6J 1Y8
www.spottedcowpress.ab.ca

ISBN: 0-9694665-4-4

This book was printed and bound in Canada by Diversified Printing Services, Edmonton, Alberta. It has been set in Adobe Garamond and ITC Officina Sans, and printed on Graphika Zinc White stock.

Designed by Melanie Eastley, Edmonton, Alberta.

Composition by Lu Ziola, Edmonton, Alberta.

Cover Photo: Players from Prelate, Saskatchewan, hockey team, 1931. Left to right: Paul Martin, Abe Liebowich, unknown, Slim Weist, Pete Martin.

Photo provided by Paul Martin.

Preface

Now that I live in North Carolina, I seldom see temperatures below freezing; such infrequent events cause a spate of news stories on how to keep the family pets from suffering from frostbite and how to protect your exposed pipes. And, consequently, there isn't much talk of hockey here. Colleagues stare blankly at me when I enthuse about the Oilers' last win or when I duck out of a function early to see the last two periods of an important game. Most times, when I tell people I'm editing a book on hockey, the reply is usually something like "You aren't from around here, are you?" No, I'm not and I'm not likely to ever be. No matter how long I've lived here or how much I like it in North Carolina, I wasn't raised with NASCAR and Tar Heel basketball; I grew up chasing a frozen black disk. Maybe it's true that you can't go home again, but it's also true that you can't take home out of you either. For me, hockey is part of home.

That idea may have been in the back of my mind when I proposed this collection in the spring of 1997 to Jerome Martin at Spotted Cow Press. To be honest, I'm not sure. All I remember is that we were in Edmonton, drinking coffee and discussing the final details for my book, *Beneath the Horse's Eye*, which was also published by Spotted Cow. My impending move to Greenville was on my mind, as well as the coincidental transformation of the Hartford Whalers into the Carolina Hurricanes. I asked Jerome what he thought about a collection of new writing on hockey. He immediately took to the idea and we arranged to put out a call for submissions in the coming months. *Ice* was beginning to take shape.

We placed ads in *Books in Canada* and *Poets & Writers,* crossing our fingers that the vibrant writing about hockey we knew was out there would arrive in my mailbox. And arrive it did, the initial trickle quickly becoming a deluge. News of the collection spread to the Saskatchewan Writers' Guild and *Word,* to name only a couple of the many places our contributors heard about *Ice*. The office staff at the English department began to grumble about the amount of mail I received; I almost got a coveted large mailbox out of the deal. As I read through the submissions, I was immediately overwhelmed by the quality of the work and astounded at the variety of perspectives. There were tales of the minor leagues, homages to professional players, memories of youth, connections between parents and children, and descriptions of not only the grace of hockey, but also its terrible beauty. I read poetry and prose of current and former players, of both parents and children of players, of long-time fans, of recent converts. Some of the contributors were reverential in tone, some were philosophical, while others approached their subjects with humor; all of them were filled with energy for the game. From both the volume of submissions and the passions contained in them it is obvious that hockey is an important part of not only my life, but the lives of a lot of people around both Canada and the United States (of the 43 contributors, 23 are from Canada and 20 are from the United States).

. . .

These days I live with heat. Last week the meteorologist on Channel 7 mentioned a cold front – that meant a forecast of only 89, a welcomed break from almost two weeks of temperatures in the high 90s. Hot. Sticky. Air so thick I imagine it will cushion my fall if I pass out from heat exhaustion. Hockey weather. At least it is for me right now as I sit in my air-conditioned office, the cool wafting over me as I drift through the images of hockey that are presented here in

Ice: New Writing on Hockey. I'm no longer in the present, no longer in Greenville, dreading the walk to my car and the cool air that will barely come before I am home. Reading these poems, short stories, and essays, I'm transported back to Amisk, to the arena where I grew up playing hockey. The ice is natural – no real need for artificial ice in rural Alberta – ridges forming along the boards as water drips from the metal walls – a sure sign of the end of hockey season. The dressing room offers a bit of heat, a brief respite from the cold that fills my lungs and numbs my toes. As soon as I can stand it, I am back on the ice, passing the puck to whoever happens to be there tonight. Back then my life was governed by the weather, the beginning and the end of the season dictated by the mercury alone. I not only lived with cold, I welcomed it.

As I read through the collection again, North Carolina heat hanging over me like a defenceman I can't shake, I feel a little cooler, a little closer to home. It would be too great a task to point out all that thrills me about this collection. Let's just say that I know you will enjoy reading about hockey in the words of these authors. The writing is fresh and I think you will enjoy the range of perspectives offered on the game. After reading *Ice*, you will know a little more about hockey and, if you are like me, a little more about yourself.

I want to take this opportunity to thank Jerome at Spotted Cow Press for giving me the opportunity to edit this collection, Melanie and Lu at Spotted Cow for their creativity and sensitivity in designing the book, Randal Martoccia for his assistance in proofreading the manuscript, and my wife, Heidi, for her support and advice. Finally, I would like to thank the office staff at the English department at East Carolina University for putting up with my unusual volume of mail. It was for a good cause.

Dale Jacobs
Greenville, North Carolina
July, 1998

A Note on the Text

Since the contributors to this collection live and write in both Canada and the United States, there arose the question of which spellings to use. In order to be true to the spirit of each contributor's words, I have endeavored to maintain the variants between Canadian and American spellings throughout the text. Inconsistencies therefore appear from one piece of writing to another, but have been included to maintain the integrity of the text as a whole.

Contents

John B. Lee

Hockey Heart

His hockey heart
beats alone in the air
the surest player
on the pond of dreams
a boy
one skate boot on the bench
one on the foot
his fingers stiff
blowing his brittle hands
to get the frost out of the joints
always the last to leave
reliving the game, lost or won,
curing his mistakes
thinking of tomorrow
as if it were already yesterday
knowing that everything happens twice
once in the present
once in the past.

Gerald Hill

Anecdote of the Hockey Game

When a twelve-year-old boy, early for his ice time,
enters Dressing Room 8, picks a spot
to dump his equipment and sit down
while the old-timers pack up and leave,
a man named Roger, number 27, a man from Saskatchewan,
takes the opportunity to speak to the boy. *I'll tell you*
a few things he says. *Listen.*

Out on the ice the kid plays quieter than usual,
can't get him to say a single word, can't see
where he is. Sometimes you hear
his skates behind, then ahead. The kid
skates for miles, doesn't mind darkness
or light, doesn't mind what gets in his way,
the masked faces, the red and blue lines.
He never gets where he's going but is always there,
looking for the loose puck, driving it home.

Toward the end of the third period with the game at its darkest,
he breaks across the blue line, no one
from him to the goalie, infinite time
to settle inside his next few moves. He breaks
in alone and lights up the red light just like
the man from Saskatchewan told him.

Thomas Michael McDade

The Consolation

My uncle said
you had to lace
the hockey skates,
hand-me-downs
from my cousin,
with rawhide.
Since there was no rink,
project kids played
on a swamp
that was half dump:
tires sticking
through the ice
like the best
seats in the house.
There was a washing
machine
with a wringer
and 55-gallon drums
in varying degrees
of exposure
that might check
or kill you.
My goal was crafted
from an old love seat.

I borrowed a stick
said to have once
been Rhode Island
Reds property.
But the puck
my eye stopped
hit like the NHL
was behind it.
Curled up one-eyed,
my skates looked
as new as
their rawhide laces
and the ice
they rested on
could have been
in Boston Garden.

Brian Turner

Of Hipchecks, Highsticks, and Yellowjackets

More than anything my father wanted me out on the ice with a hockey stick and a puck. But I was a runt with bad eyesight and weak ankles, deficiencies my father, an honored athlete, must have found hard to bear. In all the memorabilia that celebrated his exploits nothing was so vivid to me as the caricature of "Wild Bill" Turner, an All Star hockey selection for Springfield, Massachusetts, 1939. The caricature was executed in the classic style – my father's huge noggin in profile perched on a tiny, generic hockey player's body. I remember thinking how much hair he had, how dashing he looked on his cartoon skates.

I was four the first time I went out on the ice with my father's team. I dropped down from the player's box and skidded wildly about, arms flailing, as the players swooshed by like jet-propelled giants. The ceiling spun overhead, and before I knew it, I was on my back, having cracked my head.

"Get me off this crazy ice," I cried.

It wasn't until my teens that I tried to play hockey again. I joined the pick-up games on a nearby pond, but only played goal, and only if I could wear galoshes instead of skates. We had a rule since none of us wore cups or helmets – no lifting. So I stretched out across the mouth of the goal whenever the puck came near me, using my body to block every shot. One day, whether on purpose or by accident, someone lifted the puck and caught me in the throat, and I was unable to speak for an hour. That was when I gave up hockey forever, with or without skates, and I've never set foot on ice again.

Still, I loved to watch hockey. I loved the speed of the game, the booming slap shots, the kick saves. I had grown up going to games at the Eastern States Coliseum back in the days when Eddie Shore owned the Springfield Indians, when the Indians won the Calder Cup three years running. Every season of my youth seemed to have a championship waiting at the end of it, and it wasn't until later that I realized this wasn't the natural order of things.

My father was hockey coach of an obscure school with an overweening name, American International College. A.I.C. had been founded in 1886 for the purpose of educating French Canadians who came down from Quebec to work in the mills of western Massachusetts. The school also had a religious mission – to convert the Catholics, to comfort the Protestants – hence its original, quite literal name, "French Protestant College." Eventually, the trustees voted to change the name to something less unwieldy, but American International College may not have been the ideal choice.

My father took advantage of the school's Canadian connection to recruit gifted, if flawed, players from Ontario and Quebec. In the process he put together a powerful Division II hockey team with players whose judgment and discipline could charitably be called "unsound." These flawed players were the best chance my father had to win a championship, and so, ever the sportsman, he accepted the risk. His decision to take that risk had unpleasant consequences, and even in his triumph there was a hint of disgrace.

To hear my father tell it, the early years of A.I.C. hockey were marked by dramatic losses to powerhouses like Boston University, and unlikelier victories over Cornell and Army.

When A.I.C. won a big game, it was a triumph of the little guy, and when A.I.C. lost, malevolent forces were at work, usually the referees. So many times, it seemed, my father's teams fell short of greatness, giving way to better financed, more powerful foes. In recollecting those days my father emphasized the long odds, the last, desperate moments when coaches like Snooks Kelley and Ned Harkness threw everything they had at plucky, little A.I.C..

My father also claimed that his earliest teams wore uniforms fashioned from textile remnants. This strikes me as unlikely now. It's true that A.I.C. hockey had some fairly bizarre methods of fund-raising. For a time my father's players ran a dry cleaning business, "Hockey Cleaners." I can't imagine the name being an inducement. Who wants hockey players doing their dry cleaning? In fact, the players didn't do the cleaning; they took in the orders and shipped the clothes to a cleaner a block away. Had they advertised this practice, the business might have lasted longer; but they didn't, so it flopped.

And that wasn't the only unorthodox thing about A.I.C. hockey. I can remember my childhood perplexity over the A.I.C. mascot, the Yellow Jacket. I didn't object to the Yellow Jacket just because it was an insect, but rather the cartoon on the players' uniforms, a smirking, winking, winged creature with a stinger aimed at a puck. Nor did I find the three-dimensional version all that inspiring either, the little woman who dressed up as a Yellow Jacket for games, even if she did wear golden boxing gloves and made punching gestures as she cavorted in the aisles.

I loved to hide and seek in the cavernous old coliseum where A.I.C. played its home games. The building smelled of hot dogs and popcorn and peanuts, like a movie theater with all the lights on and without heat. There were no laws against smoking and the fumes of cigars or pipes mixed with cigarette smoke, all of it rising in a haze toward the ceiling where the championship banners of the Springfield Indians were displayed. Before the game I'd go into the locker room where the air was sweet with oranges and liniment. I was fascinated by the ripping sound of tape being torn from a roll as players wrapped their sticks, and freely helped myself to oranges and hot chocolate.

Half the time I wasn't watching the game, especially before my parents realized that I needed glasses. But even if I couldn't see, I could hear the bang and rattle of a puck along the boards and all those skates whizzing down the ice. I even loved the appearance of the Zamboni machine between periods, and I imagined myself at the wheel, transforming the chafed surface into a glistening, clear expanse.

For some reason, when I was about six, I went through a phase where I rolled up my program and used it as a megaphone to razz my father's players in my piping, high-pitched child's voice. It was a strange way to behave, especially since I was on their side. My father's players were the only players I knew, so I insisted on calling them bums and jerks, hooting and booing until my mother explained to me that this wasn't sort of thing the coach's son should do. I guess it didn't seem like such a big deal, being the coach's son. Later I had the grace to wonder how the coach felt about having a son like me.

. . .

I went to A.I.C. on a tuition waiver and worked at the sports bureau as a publicist. In that capacity I kept stats, called in scores, and traveled with the team to remote parts of New England. The long miles of wintry terrain through which the bus traveled tried my patience at times, especially after a tough loss, but I enjoyed the waves of jade-green ice flowing down the rock-face and the clearings that opened in the otherwise unbroken winter forests, usually a lake buried by snow.

This was the 1968-1969 season, and my father was bullish on the Canadian line – Mike Egoroff, Ian Caldwell, Yves DeRome, and Dave Forbes. They were skating demons, these Canadians, savage, cunning, fearless. We also had a Canadian goalie of considerable ability, Donny Young. But for all their talent the Canadians were far from perfect; if they had been perfect, they would have been on their way to the NHL, not playing for a two-bit New England college. Still, they did everything so naturally on the ice they made the local players look slow and klutzy. They had the aura of real heroes, cocky as can be.

My favorite Canadian was Mike Egoroff, "Igor" people called him. Right away I liked him because his eyeglasses were thick as ashtrays. He cut quite a figure on the ice and off. Not to put too fine a point on it, he was fat. When Igor charged down the ice and bent his stick back and brought all that weight to bear upon the precise point of impact, only the most courageous opponents held their ground. Igor was big as a rhino and just as near-sighted, and that added an element of uncertainty to his slap-shot. His manners left something to be desired. It might have been his bad eyes, but he went about campus scowling, his voice low and gruff, and if he spoke at all, he grunted.

By contrast his line-mate Ian Caldwell was pleasant and polite. A compactly built, modest man with a wife and a young child, Caldwell chose not to pursue a professional career, but parlayed his skills as a defenseman and penalty killer into a college degree. Unlike Igor, Caldwell never failed to say hello to me as we passed on our way to classes, and while I appreciated his friendliness, his open manner somehow lessened his mystique.

The senior captain, Yves DeRome, was the oldest member of the team, almost 26, nearly too old to qualify for ECAC play. With smooth strides he carried the puck end to end before taking a wrist shot, almost always on net. A fine penalty-killer, and crafty complement to Caldwell, DeRome easily kept the puck in the opponents' end. Like Caldwell, DeRome had a young wife. I wondered if it was the custom among Canadians to marry young, or whether DeRome and Caldwell were precocious.

My father acknowledged that DeRome had a habit of applying the blade of his stick to the ribs of opposing players. DeRome has this problem, my father would say, his voice lowered. "He's like a guy who has to make a pass at every woman," he said. "He can't let a guy go by without giving him a jab." For a time DeRome's stick work was too quick for the referees to catch. But the referees knew something was going on because of the frequency with which players chased DeRome down the ice in an attempt, usually futile, to repay him in kind. After the word got around the division, it didn't matter whether the referees saw the infraction or not, they called the penalties anyway.

In addition to veterans like DeRome and Egoroff, and the steady, cool-headed Caldwell, my father recruited a spectacular young player named Dave Forbes from Lachine, Quebec. My father, who was not given to hyperbole, said that Forbes was the best college player he had ever seen. Forbes, he told me, had a chance to make the NHL.
I should have known that a player who was "the best" yet who was being recruited to play at A.I.C. had to have something wrong with him. Still, my father said only good things about Forbes, and when he showed up at our house, I was surprised to see he wasn't much bigger than I was.
My father put Forbes up on a cot between my brother's bed and mine. We were talking in the dark before going to

sleep, when Dave asked, "Hey, how come you don't talk funny?"

By which he meant I didn't talk like John F. Kennedy. It's a common misconception that everyone from Massachusetts talks with a Boston accent. Springfield's 90 miles west of Boston, though it's hard to tell that to people from outside New England. The Boston accent stops somewhere around Worcester, and Springfield's another 35 miles west of Worcester. People from Springfield speak the way upstate New Yorkers do, with a hint of Connecticut, an accent nondescript enough to be considered "normal."

I had never seen my father so excited about a player as he was about Dave Forbes, but it was something of a devil's bargain. It was bad enough that DeRome would jab someone in the ribs and sail by, but Forbes had a tendency to take the blade of his stick to a player's face and do real damage. It didn't happen often, but when it did it was a terrible thing to see. There was something clinical about it, the way he cold-bloodedly cut his victim up like a surgeon with an extra-large scalpel. Apparently he'd done this before and had forfeited his chances at playing with the Canadian youth teams, the training ground for the NHL. But my father prided himself on his ability to handle problem players, so he was confident he could handle Dave Forbes. Besides, more than anything he wanted to win a division championship, and he saw Forbes and the Canadian Line as his main chance.

. . .

Not everything from that season could be called A.I.C.'s finest hour or mine. In fact, some of the more embarrassing moments are what I remember best. All in all the season had, well, character not unlike that of the team – volatile and dangerous, but never boring. In the end the guys had enough courage to go all the way to the finals, leaving a trail of half-wrecked motels and bruised, scarred opponents. And yet, in the heat of the game, when everything was on the line, the Yellow Jackets had a tendency to fall apart. That was what made the 1968-1969 team so baffling and unpredictable.

The first time they fell apart was at the Codfish Bowl, a tournament held in Boston during Christmas break. Since the tournament lasted the weekend, we stayed at a cheesy mid-town motel. I shared a room with whatever player was unfortunate enough to be stuck with me. Since I was the coach's son, no one wanted me for a roommate. Nor did I care to hang around with my father and his assistants since doing so would only reinforce my reputation as "coach's son." Just opening the door to my father's motel room was an assault upon the senses. His assistants and he sat around in their underwear, drinking vodka tonics and smoking cigars as they plotted hockey strategy.

A lot was riding on the outcome of that night's final. If A.I.C. won the Codfish Bowl, we were almost certain to make the playoffs. Once we had been guaranteed a berth, we could rest the Canadians and bring along some of the other players. If we lost, then we had to struggle through the toughest part of the schedule, a series of brutal away games, and the Canadians would continue to do double-duty, playing their regular line and doing most of the penalty-killing – when they weren't in the box themselves.

The Yellow Jackets had reached the final of the Codfish Bowl by edging out Bowdoin. It was always a pleasure to beat Williams or Amherst, Bowdoin or Colby or Bates. These "selective" schools tended to look down their noses at A.I.C. To remind us of our less than elite status, the Amherst and Williams kids would sing the Mickey Mouse Club theme, substituting the first three letters, "A-I-C – K-E-Y. M-O-U-S-E."

But we had been beating the daylights out of our Ivy League opponents all season, and that had its compensations.

Now we faced a good, lunch-bucket team, Boston State, a team we had dominated in previous encounters, and we dominated them for two periods of the final game. The Boston State team wasn't as flashy or powerful as we were, and the Canadian line poured through their defense and put a flurry of shots on net. It was 6-2 with five minutes to go, and I was up in the press box ready to call in the win.

Suddenly, DeRome's jabs weren't sneaky enough to fool the referees, and he and several other players took stupid penalties. On the receiving end of consecutive power plays, our goalie, Donny Young, was getting beat again and again. The time had ticked down and we had a goal lead. Before a face off at the other end, Young took off his mask and mopped his face. I could see that he had lost his Canadian swagger and verve. The other team was having all the fun now; they had the momentum. Boston State tied the game, then won in the first minute of overtime. My final image was of Young as the winning goal slipped past him, and his agony as he held himself up with both hands on the top bar of the cage.

It was a sobering ride home, deep into the night, pulling into campus, everyone heading off to his room at 1 a.m. Sitting beside my father, not speaking, I could tell he was shaken. The collapse in the Codfish Bowl had implications for the rest of the season. If the team got into the habit of folding, especially when a trophy was on the line, all the talent in the world wouldn't help the Yellow Jackets make the playoffs.

My father made a move that took me by surprise. Donny Young had been the starting goalie for three years and had set several college records. Graceful and quick, he seemed to be everywhere the puck was – but only for the first two periods and only if we were ahead. I didn't see that we could do much about Donny other than let him play. Our back-up goalie, Kenny Welch, had been gravely injured at a pizza shop off campus. Some nut ran in with a hammer and bashed Kenny over the head – boom, no warning. Kenny didn't know the guy, and the guy got away, so no one ever found out why he did it. Kenny was still in the hospital with a fractured skull. That left us with our third-string goalie, a Springfield boy named John Normand. Surely, my father wouldn't put *him* in the goal!

John Normand had a sleepy look in his eyes and a slow way of talking, and he didn't move all that quickly on the ice or off. By any measure he was mediocre goalie, but he had one quality that worked to his advantage – he appeared to be oblivious to what was going on around him, and this gave him an aura of self-possession no matter how desperate things got. I wouldn't say John lacked confidence, really, but he didn't have that swagger, that cockiness of the Canadians. I was used to seeing that swagger, and it unnerved me that the team's fate now depended on someone so untried. John Normand had given up an average of more than five goals a game on the occasions he played. While we had a powerful offense, and an adequate defense, I doubted we could consistently score six or more goals a game in the run to the playoffs. If we lost with Donny in the net, I figured it would be the team's fault; but with John Normand, it would be the coach's fault. His decision, his fault. But my father put John in the net anyway.

. . .

In early February we traveled to play Colby College in Waterville, Maine. It was too far to return the same night, so we stayed at a Holiday Inn. For the Yellow Jackets of A.I.C., a Holiday Inn with vibrating beds and a heated pool was heady stuff. We paired off, and as usual no one was eager to share with me: "Coach's son," as the Canadians said, leaving out the article, "coach's son. You stay with coach's son. Not me."

John Normand took the fall. If he minded, he didn't say so. I'm not sure how he did it, but within two minutes of getting in our room he managed to stuff up the toilet, and it backed up, and whether it embarrassed him or offended his sensibility, he left and didn't come back. So I ended up with the room to myself, which would have been nice but nobody came by to fix the toilet.

There were hundreds and hundreds of crazed Colby fans packed into the stands that night. I swear that Colby didn't heat their rink, and the breath of the crowd rose in explosive puffs that merged into a cloud of steam when everyone got excited, which was fairly often. Both teams played tight and clean because a berth in the playoffs was up for grabs. The game ended in almost complete silence, the best you can hope for on the road – a 5-4 victory for the Yellow Jackets. How John Normand stopped the last shots, I'll never know. According to my stats, he was due to let one by, but he stopped them, as oblivious to his accomplishment as he was to the pressure. When the game was over I called in the scores to the media outlets of Western Massachusetts and returned to my room with the stuffed up toilet.

I watched TV, went to bed. Before long I was listening to the unmistakable sounds of a party. The sound of running and hooting and laughing filled the night. It must have been zero outside, but I don't think anyone was feeling the cold. It would get quiet for a while, then suddenly there would be the sound of doors opening and shutting with a crash, and more howling and laughter. That was when the phone rang.

"Brian, Brian," someone growled on the other end.

I mumbled, "What?"

"Brian, Brian, it's me, it's Igor."

It must have been two in the morning. "Who?"

"Egoroff," the voice on the phone said.

Igor! Igor was calling me, the coach's son. I couldn't believe it.

"Brian," Igor said, "we want you to come down for a drink."

Even with Igor on the line, giving me permission to join the team for a drink, I hesitated.

"Brian," he said, "I like you, Brian, no matter what the other guys say. "

But it was too cold out, too early in the morning, and I couldn't hold my liquor. My nickname was "One Beer Brian," because I tended to get sloppy after a beer. Besides, I didn't really want to know what the players were doing running up and down the outdoor walkway leading to our rooms. Nor did I wish to be seen drunk – after all, I was "coach's son" and had a reputation to uphold.

I had left the door unlocked in case John Normand showed up, which he didn't. After a time the door crashed open and wind came rushing in from the parking lot. There standing in the icy darkness was Igor! A big pink mountain of flesh. He was stripped to his briefs like a giant baby in diapers, standing in the hellish winter of Waterville, Maine. There was a look of terror in his staring eyes, though that may have been because he wasn't wearing his glasses.

"Brian, Brian," he said, hopping from one bare foot to another. "They're after me. They're going to do something to me, I know it. They're after me."

He slammed the door and pressed against it with his shoulder, as if the whole team might charge through the door at any moment and tear off his briefs.

“Brian,” he said, “they’re animals, they’re animals.”

He mumbled for several minutes, pressed against the door. Without his glasses he squinted helplessly about the room. This, I said to myself, is Igor? This is the man who would be King of the ECAC? The man with the thunder and lightning slap shot?

Igor went into the bathroom.

“Igor,” I said, “don’t use the toilet!”

It was too late. He’d flushed already. A flood came from under the bathroom door.

“*Brian,*” he shouted, rushing from the bathroom and standing tiptoe in the spreading mess. In a disgusted voice he said, “I can’t believe what a pig you are.”

With that, he opened the door, took a look both ways, and seeing the coast was clear, he ran steaming into the night, leaving footprints that soon turned to ice.

According to police reports, some of the players stripped the night manager and threw him into the heated pool, which, as it turned out, was what they intended to do to me had I showed up at Igor’s invitation. When I declined, they turned on Igor. The total cost to the college, defrayed among the players and spread out over several semesters, came to more than $700, a not inconsiderable sum in those days.

. . .

On the ice and off the A.I.C Yellow Jackets were known as rough customers, brutes and louts and madmen. The opposing teams came into a game with that in mind, and so did the officials. Too many of the Yellow Jackets – especially Igor, a tempting target – were spending time in the penalty box; the other teams were getting more chances to win than they deserved. And then there was sleepy, slow-moving, stand-up John Normand in the goal. But Forbes, Igor, Caldwell, and DeRome poured pucks into the opposing net at a rate that kept us a little bit ahead. The race to make the playoffs was tight, and in spite of all the talent we had, we weren't a shoe-in because the other schools had talent too, plenty of it, and they had discipline – usually.

Discipline broke down on all sides at the notorious "riot" at Salem State, and it broke down for me, too. What was my job? To put A.I.C. hockey in the best light. Doing that's a lot easier than keeping a puck out of the net or putting a shot between a goalie's glove and the post.

So how did I do?

I choked big time.

The team bus rolled into Salem during a blizzard. Blizzards have always been a quiet, private time in my experience, a chance to scale back life's complexities, to turn up the heat and wait for the weather to clear and read a book. But I had a job to do, we had a playoff berth to clinch. Salem State was out of the running, so only the hardiest, most crazed fans showed up for the game. The bleachers were almost empty during the first period, but as news spread on the student radio station about the beating we were giving the local boys, several dozen angry students trudged from the dorms to the rink.

We had started the game off by pouring six or seven goals into the net. By the third period not much was at stake, and that led to some loose play. Our guys were as guilty as anyone, taunting the other team and giving them the business with their sticks. By the start of the third period the already outraged fans were on their feet, screaming abuse and throwing debris. Then, midway through the period, with A.I.C. up 12-2, both teams cleared their benches in the biggest melee of the season.

The officials were determined to take control of the game. For some reason they decided to throw almost everyone out of the game. When the officials got through tossing guys, A.I.C. had only four eligible players, the goalie and three other guys, none of them our best. The game had more than 10 minutes to go with our side at a permanent two-man disadvantage. We didn't even have a second line!

Sitting in the penalty box to represent all the ejected A.I.C. players was the captain, DeRome. The incensed fans surrounded the box, giving him a piece of their collective mind. Now and then he would turn and wink, purse his lips and blow kisses as the fans pounded with their fists on the Plexiglas.

Time and time again, our remaining three players collapsed back onto the net. Along with the rest of the team John Normand had been sent to the showers. Donny Young was back in the goal for the first time since the Codfish fiasco. The puck went past him again and again, and since we were permanently short-handed, the pressure never let up. This was not the sort of situation at which Young excelled, and I found myself wishing we had Normand back.

Now it was 12-10 with seconds left, so it looked as if we would escape with a victory, a sloppy one, marred by brawls and penalties, but a victory nonetheless. The prospect of losing after having made an amazing comeback was driving the Salem State fans berserk. That was when someone in the stands took a crutch from a guy with a cast on his leg. Given the events of the last hour, the guy with the broken leg might have volunteered it as a weapon. In any case the fan who took the crutch ran down to the penalty box and used it to clobber DeRome over the helmet.

Yves must have thought the roof was falling. The fate of our second-string goalie, poor Kenny Welch, in that pizza shop off campus must have flashed through his mind. His head scrunched down into his pads, then popped up again and wobbled. He was quick enough to duck the next blow that landed on his shoulder pads. Apparently unharmed, he jumped up on the rink wall and stood there with his stick up, like Zorro fighting off the bad guys. He waved his stick at the guy holding the crutch and poked him now and then with that little deft touch of his. Enraged fans were jumping onto the ice now, trying to grab Yves from behind, and so, still perched on the rink wall, he spun around, slashing at them with his stick, holding them at bay. The officials had had all they could take, blowing their whistles and waving their arms for the scorekeeper and timekeeper to stop the game for good.

I was on my feet in the press box, shouting out, "It's a riot!"

Now I had seen riots before. This was the winter of 1968-69 after all, at the height of the Vietnam War. King and Kennedy had been assassinated, the Democratic convention in Chicago had erupted in nationally televised violence. I had gone to Washington for an anti-war demonstration and watched helplessly as my fellow protesters were chased down by cops and beaten. I made my escape from D.C. that day in a bus filled with injured, bleeding, half-blinded marchers. So I knew what a riot was and this hockey game, rough as it was, was not a riot. Still it was an impressive display of misbehavior as these things go. The Salem police were sliding around the ice and wrestling with the fans and making arrests. Campus security recommended that we stay in the locker room until the rink had been cleared, which required two paddy wagons. When we left, we formed a circle with my father and me in the middle, and the team forming a phalanx, their sticks out just in case there was a mob waiting. But there wasn't a mob. Just the bus warmed up and ready to take us home.

If the story had ended there, I would have been OK. But I had made the mistake of calling the local news station, WWLP-TV and blurting out, "A.I.C. beats Salem State, 12-10. There was a riot."

"A riot," said Bill Rasmussen, at that time a lowly sportscaster, later to become rich as the founder of ESPN. "Mind if I record you?"

For someone who prided himself on his "media" savvy, I said some truly stupid things, going into all the sensational details as if sitting at a bar with my cronies. Rasmussen was delighted and made sure that the story led the 11 o'clock news. The A.I.C. public relations director, my soon-to-be-beleaguered boss, described for me the effect of turning on the TV and hearing A.I.C. hockey mentioned before the national news. When he heard the word riot, his stomach knotted as he considered the hellish week of damage control ahead of him. In the morning the story was on the front page, not of the sports section, but right beside the news about the latest screw-up in Vietnam: "A.I.C. Yellow Jackets Riot!" People imagined a mob of hockey players in black and yellow, hockey sticks for stingers, running amok in the streets of Salem–so much for public relations.

"Brian," my boss said, having called me to his office, "there is a word that does not exist in the lexicon of public relations. And that word is 'riot.'"

"Sorry."

"You can call it an altercation, you can call it a spirited encounter, a melee, a brawl, a fight."

"O.K."

"But never, ever a riot–!""

The one person who didn't give me grief was my father, the coach. He'd give me grief about a lot of things, yet when it really counted, when I had really done something stupid, he didn't seem to feel the need to rub my nose in it. He let me know I was wrong, but he left it up to my boss to give me hell or fire me (which my boss did as soon the season was over). The coach left it up to his players to let me know I had done them a disservice; and he left the rest up to me.

"Coach's son," the Canadians groused. "Coach's son tells everyone we riot."

. . .

I was demoted even before the season ended, reduced to announcing goals and penalties over the public address system, but after my blunder at Salem State I was glad to have any role to play. I had seen the Yellow Jackets in their glory and in their less glorious moments, too, so I wanted to be there for the championship final, come what may. On the morning of the playoff final I could hardly eat my breakfast. I found it hard to walk, my legs were so rubbery, my breathing was rapid and shallow. Later, as the hour drew near for the opening face-off, my nervousness shrank to a tiny frozen core of terror that made it difficult for me to function.

I kept thinking about the players. I had come to realize that my father's players weren't heroes; they were just kids like me, only bigger and stronger, and meaner. They were talented and fallible. Maybe a little too fallible. They had talent, sure, but could they overcome their wilder tendencies? Could they resist taking bone-headed penalties? Could they stand up to another rush at the last moment by a team of spirited underdogs? I was frightened for my father, afraid that his dream of being the best in the division would vanish forever, with John Normand half-asleep in the goal.

The final game against Norwich drew more people than I had seen at the Coliseum since the Calder Cup series and the Indians' hey-day of the late 50s. Norwich was seeded fourth, and they'd beaten our nemesis from the previous year's playoffs, defending champion Merrimack. The cadets of Norwich had stuck it to us earlier in the season, and we'd returned the compliment, both games decided by a single goal. Still they were the underdogs, just like Boston State in the Codfish Bowl – God help us!

Norwich scored the first goal of the game. Normand let the puck go past him with such nonchalance that I groaned in despair. But we came back and banged in three goals. With Normand in the goal, however, we needed more than that. Norwich was fast, and they could score again, and they did, taking back the lead. That was the way the game went, back and forth, and every time Norwich brought the puck down, John Normand came out of the net to cut down the angle. He stood there, looking awkward, and I just crossed my fingers, sighing with relief whenever he cleared the puck.

At one point I was so caught up in the action that I forgot to let go of the microphone, and couldn't believe my ears when I heard my own voice come booming down from the huge speaker system, filling the coliseum: "Come on, A.I.C.!"

The crowd fell silent for a second. The players looked at me from across the ice; the linesman blew his whistle and skated over to the announcer's box to give me a warning. My father scowled from the bench, and I shrugged, flapping my hands to show that my all-too-public cheer had been inadvertent. Still, just to be safe, I handed the microphone over to someone else, taking it back only to make announcements of goals and assists, of which there were too many for Norwich to suit me.

Every time A.I.C. took a penalty I thought for sure this was it. But if you had to have four guys on the ice, the four we put out there were exceptional – the Canadian penalty-killers, Igor, DeRome, Caldwell, and super sophomore Dave Forbes. Back and forth the players went, crashing into the boards, lifting the net off its pins, and the shots sailed through the air and rattled off the glass, and every time I opened my eyes there was John Normand, still standing, and we were still in the game. The fans were on their feet because the game was so wide-open, and it was getting to the point that neither team deserved to lose.

With minutes to go it was 6-6. Normand had already exceeded his average goals allowed, but for once even I felt the stats were irrelevant. Suddenly, there was traffic around the mouth of the Norwich net. For one instant no one moved. Igor stood alone, his legs big as trees. His stomach preceded him, giving him a center of gravity that made it difficult for Norwich to shove him off the play. The puck squirted out in front, and he put it between the goalie's pads with a flip. It trickled over the line, and to this day I believe Igor was born to put the red light on at that moment. Now it was up to John Normand and the defense to keep us ahead, and by defense, I mean the whole team. I don't think there was a player who took the lead for granted – not after the Codfish Bowl fiasco.

Norwich fired up the ice and put sharp, hard shots on net. Again and again our guys steered the puck clear or went down and took a shot in the body. The last Norwich rush came with only seconds left. The center broke free, a stride ahead of the A.I.C. defenders. John Normand came out one more time, standing up with all the pressure bearing down upon him. I thought for sure the Norwich center would deke, skate past him, and make an easy shot. But Normand skated straight ahead, a move so unexpected it may have confused the Norwich center. He could have skated straight over Normand if he wanted to. He was big enough, and Normand was fifteen or twenty feet out of the crease. Instead they both stopped, hesitated, and the center took the shot head on. Caldwell, who had caught up with the play by now, threw himself in front of the shot, partially deflecting it. The puck skipped up into Normand's chest and popped in the air. The players stood ready to swing their sticks when the puck came within reach. But Normand raised his glove, slapped at the puck, juggling it just enough to make my heart skip. Then he gathered the puck to his chest, cradling it as if it was something to be treasured. He fell to his knees, rolled into fetal position, and players on both sides fell on him. The siren went off. We had won.

John Normand had stood his ground, more or less. The great and terrible Igor had scored the winning goal, not with one of his slapshots, but with an almost casual flick of his stick. Yes, Igor, the guy running around the Holiday Inn in Waterville, Maine in his underwear – my hero. And the big guns – Forbes with two goals and an assist, and DeRome, and Caldwell – and all the guys who weren't exactly stars, they all did their bit. So they fell down together in one big pile and celebrated.

I ran to the bench and took the coach in my arms, and we danced up and down the aisle of the coliseum, as the little woman in the Yellow Jacket outfit with the golden boxing gloves joined us, pummeling us with tiny congratulatory punches.

Back then I didn't know what I know now. The upcoming season was to be my father's last, his worst ever, and a publicity nightmare. In a cost-cutting move, the college administration scaled back the hockey program. The college was experiencing financial difficulty anyway, so the cuts might have happened in any case, but it didn't help that my father's players had brought the college such notoriety, a situation for which I had to assume some responsibility.

Dave Forbes jumped to the pros after his junior year. He wasn't going to play as a senior anyway, because the ECAC had suspended him for the 1970-71 season for carving up the face of an opposing player in a meaningless game. Then, at the height of his career with the Bruins, he disgraced himself again, becoming the only player to be indicted for assault and battery on the ice. I couldn't bring myself to watch the news, the story of his trial, or what he had done to the eye of a North Star player. To this day my father wonders if he failed Forbes somehow, failed to impress upon him the importance of controlling his impulses. When he says stuff like that, I'll remind him that most of the kids he coached turned out to be great guys, but of course he keeps thinking about the one that got away. Or he thinks of Mike Egoroff who after he graduated was diagnosed with leukemia and died a few years later. Igor's death still gets to my father. It gets to my father more than it gets to me, since for me Igor will always be larger than life, a hero of the Canadian line. But for my father Igor was like a son. And so was Dave Forbes.

I remember the 1968-69 season with a complicated pleasure. Maybe it's the smell of oranges, the ripping of tape; something sets me off, and I find myself reminiscing. I realize how rare a championship is, how fortunate I was to ride on the bus, to sit in the press box, to call in the scores. It was as close as I got to being on my father's team, and I'm glad that I had that chance, because my ankles never got any stronger.

Beth Goobie

a hockey player's body

a hockey player's body is intended
as a national anthem, flag of tendons,
bones that undulate down the ice,
heart sung by crowds in the stands
hot dogs and beer in their hands, dreams
gone wrong in their mouths. as if this was
to have been a game a spectator could control
as he sways and twists in his seat,
traveling the universe, jams table game
tin figures this way and that until a wife
calls him to supper where he chews, swallows
endless stats, history building itself
into one man's flesh. *bobby hull, bobby orr,*
maurice richard skate frozen-over
rivers in each man's chest, sudden desire that
looms out of fog, soars on the knife sound
of skates; each man dances and dangles
in his sleep, wanting to follow, stoops
to memorize the pattern of blades tracked
in the ice, tries to teach this passing
of gods to his son.

a hockey player's body carries generations
of fathers who loved their fathers silenced
by wars, depression, dark windows of the brain;
fathers who pulled the muscle off their own bone
and sewed those windows closed,
opened eyes to the coming light, walked
into early morning, horizon of pure fresh-fallen
snow dawn-lit to soft pinks and blues,
stick and the swing of skates slung over a shoulder,
puck heavy in a pocket, voice of a small son
piping along at the waist, questions about angles,
how to tie his shoes. fathers who crouched
wordless in the net, nothing to speak

about lay-offs, cannon fodder, the ways a sky
can explode into a million shards of bone,
just terse wisdom for a boy wobbling on first
skates, furrowed forehead, poking at the puck.
both surrounded by the constant spirits
of their breath, it came out warm hope,
angels rising from them both, flickering
alive. moments that were unjudged,

a father and son focused, breathing morning,
movement, a puck. as evening crept down skies,
fingered at shutters, landmines of the mind,
fathers were at the tv, *hockey night in canada;*
the air in their lungs dipped and swooped
with figures on the screen. sometimes a man

lifted one moment into glory merged
with *phil esposito* coming to the net, souls
of a million canadians carried in the angle
of that stick, wishing that puck in. forgetting

to pull themselves out again, forgetting
to allow sons their own bodies, their own
dreams, tangents of blade and hip.
stooped forever in those lonely myths,
men tracing blade tracks knifed into ice,
watching their souls tremble from their lips.
moments of such wonder, odysseys to be breathed
from a ringside seat, arenas echoing
with that heartbeat of wrist shot, backhand shot,
slapshot, *he shoots he scores*!

fathers sending everything they could not hold
as thought as flesh onto the ice,
a hockey player's body is full of goals
other people score against him,
the boys the team paid to keep young,
vivid and fighting dark shut-tight doors
onto other lives. their fathers watching,
still coaching on far-off rivers, super
human sons they cannot allow to become men.

Richard Harrison

Using the Body

It's the instruction for goons, use the body, pound
the other guy rougher than his game imagines, the
body hitting home, the body the agent of policy.
When a fight begins, we say it is emotion, but after
the game, the goon speaks clearly of motive, the
momentum of play, doing what he has to do, a strict
account level in his head. Later, when he wears a
suit, when he coaches, you can see how he saw the
entire rink all along: he never looked at the puck,
the stickwork, a man's cheek when his purpose is
clear and there's open ice before him. He saw the
solid mass of a man, how the game, flimsy as a
wing, could be held at the socket where the wing
joins the body, and broken.

Joanne Merriam

Vignette from Quebec Major Juniors

A perfect desire
rises from the crowd, a heartbeat
pounding home-team! home-team!

Some expressive beauty (not
like a well-turned banister
is beautiful nor like you, my love,
are beautiful, but beautiful with the fury
of nature's chlorophyll dynamos)
comes over them,
awestruck by the terrible perfection
of the rink with its beveled edges and ice
smooth as half-sucked lozenges,
the goalies staking out territory with huge
casual parabolas, and one of their own
gets by the giant on the visiting team
and HE SHOOTS HE SCORES
a roar rising

or the occasional explosion of violence,
into which the audience, beautiful,
thrusts itself

two guys (who you just know are
the types mothers trust their daughters with
foolishly)
say YOU WANNA GO?
And YEAH. YOU WANNA GO?
gleefully throw down helmet, gloves, sticks
and go
until the final uppercut

when the crowd surges up, gorgeous.
Their mouths say O

Don Bell

Hockey Night in Métabetchouan

Look at it this way: there isn't a lot to do Sundays in Métabetchouan up on the shores of Lac St-Jean in northern Quebec. There isn't a Museum of Fine Arts: there's no Chinatown, no bookstores, no Sunday brunches. The closest movie house is in Alma, but that's a fair distance, especially in a blizzard. There's a zoo in St-Félicien, but it's closed in the winter.

There's the church, of course, but that's out by noon. You can book a room in the Motel Terrasso and have an affair, but it's a small town: sooner or later you'll get caught. You can try *poutine* – french fries topped with curd cheese and drowned in chicken barbeque sauce – at one of the *cantines* in town, but can your stomach take it? You can dig a hole in the ice on the Couchepaganiche River and fish for *ouananiche,* but how can you catch something that is too hard to pronounce?

There are no lectures, no concert halls, no poolrooms, no bingo. There's nothing much on TV. You can't shop. Only the *tabagie* and *Chez Maman Lise* are open. You can take a drive, but to where?

Let's face it, Sunday would be boring in this tranquil Lac St-Jean community, eight hours by train from Montreal. Would be but isn't. Isn't thanks to those fabulous young minstrels in the Pittsburgh Penguin colors: here they come now, charging on the ice, ready to fight to the last drop of blood and die in the rink for the honor of the town; *Mesdames et messieurs on vous présente* – the Northern Fruits of Métabetchouan!

The who? The what? By their proper name, the *SS Norfruit de Métabetchouan. SS* isn't the insignia for Hitler's special police, the *Schutzstaffel;* it stands for *Secteur Sud,* or the south sector of the lake, encompassing the area from which the players are drawn. And *Norfruit* (the name emblazoned on their yellow and black sweaters) is the name of the grossiste en fruits et *légumes* (the fruit and vegetable distributor) that has sponsored the team for the last three years.

You've heard of Saturday Night Fever at the Montreal Forum? It's nothing compared to Sunday Night Fever in Métabetchouan. The Norfruits are the local heroes, the slambangalong, frantic-rushing grinders of the five-team Saguenay-Lac St-Jean Junior "AA" hockey league. What they lack in finesse, they make up for in undiluted spirit.

Here is boondocks hockey in its rawest form, hockey as the fundamental Canadian experience. Here, the very soul of hockey can be tapped. In Métabetchouan, as in many similar-sized communities across the land, hockey isn't just a game, but a way of life, a philosophy, a religion.

Métabetchouan is a land of dairy farms, blueberries and the fighting landlocked salmon known as the *ouananiche.* To an outsider, it's like some exotic foreign country. English simply never is heard here, except in summer when an occasional tourist passes through to photograph the unusual pink granite facade of *l'Eglise St-Jérome.* Otherwise, there's as much chance as hearing Swahili in Inuvik. It's a close-knit community of 3,500 friendly souls on the banks of Lac St-Jean, and in winter la vie sociale centers around the hockey arena; the fans are dedicated and boisterous, following the ups and downs of the local team with as much enthusiasm as hard core NHL fans rooting for the Habs during the Stanley Cup.

"If there was as much interest in my concerts," says Métabetchouan's best-known citizen, pop singer Ariane Voyer, "I'd be playing to packed houses every time I perform." Voyer, in fact, says she makes it a point never to schedule a *spectacle* in any of the *boîtes* in the area if there's a hockey game the same evening.

On Sundays, there's a mass rush to the *centre sportif* for a hockey energy fix. A quarter to a third of the population will cram into the arena to watch *les Norfruits* tangle with *les Citadins d' Arvida, les Castors de Dolbeau, les Saguenéens de Chicoutimi* or, their opponents tonight, *les Marquis de Jonquière,* seven points ahead and in first place.

There's always interest when les *Marquis* are in town. Raynald Tremblay, the Norfruits' manager, recalls a playoff game – *un super-match* – a couple of years ago when 2,200 fans squeezed into the supposedly 1,000-person capacity arena at 6 P.M. for a 9 P.M. game against les Marquis, and there was even a flurry of ticket-scalping at the door.

The burning question tonight is whether *les Norfruit* can take *les Marquis* and thus reduce the lead to five points and have a crack at catching them before the end of the season. But does it matter? As one soon realizes, the peripheral events surrounding the game – the interesting *placotage* (gossip) in the arena, the smell of hot dogs, the *tirages* (raffles), the between-periods contests, the colorful P.A. announcements – are as much an attraction as the events on the ice.

So here is a report of the sidelines action in Métabetchouan, of what happens when the *SS Norfruit,* those minstrels of Lac St-Jean, meet their bitter enemies, *les Marquis de Jonquière,* in the dead of winter.

Pre-Game Show

The name "Métabetchouan" is an Indian expression meaning "that which gathers its strength before delivering itself," a reference to the course of the Métabetchouan River as it rises in Laurentides Park and flows north to Lac St-Jean. There are numerous rapids along the river's 85-mile length, and in the last few miles, it broadens, then narrows and becomes relatively still, "gathering its strength" before discharging into the lake.

The meaning may also be a metaphor for the atmosphere at *le centre sportif* before the big match against *les Marquis.* At 5:30, two hours before game time, Dany Villeneuve, the Norfruits' affable young coach, a former junior star with *les Aiglons d'Alma,* enters the room and begins his mental preparation for the game. Nervous? Not at all. "I have to stay calm and communicate this feeling to my players." It's the lull time for Dany now, as if he is "gathering his strength" in this interval before the game begins.

But his equanimity had been shattered and a feeling of turmoil had set in the previous week after two straight losses to *les Citadins d'Arvida.* In an impassioned speech, Dany had implied that a few players had been hitting the booze the night before the games.

"You have the choice of either playing for the SS or hanging around the bars," he had told them after the second loss, his eyes settling on the suspected culprits. The talk seemed to fire up the team, because they came back in their next game to thrash the *Saguenéens* and now, according to Dany, were up and ready for this big game against the league-leading Marquis.

At 6:30, the doors open and now there is a full vent of fury. *Les centre sportif* is the social seat of the community, it's the village square in winter, where you meet the friends you haven't seen all week. Here comes the rowdy Hébertville contingent, occupying one whole corner of the arena; here's the ex-cop and governor of the Norfruits, Carol Fortin; here's the sports reporter, Jean-Paul Gimaiel, distant cousin of the President of Lebanon; here are the brothers Pierre and Gilles Gagné, partners in *La Compagnie Norfruit* with the brothers Bertran and Benoit Fortin; here's Jean-Paul Ouellet, owner of the *restaurant Rond-point,* local hangout for the hockey crowd.

"Salut... hé ... salut ... grosse partie ^ soir, hein? ... ta femme, ça va? Pis les enfants?"

And here's the local barber, Jean-Louis Bilodeau, a legend in Métabetchouan. Now 75, he's been working in the same one-chair shop for 61 years, and is a survivor of the old 50-degrees-below-zero outdoor ice hockey days. Bilodeau was a goaler in the 1920s and 1930s for the old Lac St-Jean teams – *les Chameaux de Métabetchouan, les Pepsi-Colas* ... .

"We used to travel to the games by sleigh in those days," he recalls. "The rules were quite different then. A goaler wasn't allowed to go down and he couldn't glove the puck. A shutout was a rare phenomenon." Bilodeau still skates Sunday afternoons – he's the Aurèle Joliat of the region – and never misses a Norfruits' game. Coming to the arena, one suspects, is the highlight of the week for him. "It's a sickness, worse than somebody with alcohol disease," he states.

The Norfruits' Richard Belley has been named *joueur du mois* – player-of-the-month. In a dignified ceremony at centre ice, he's awarded the Molson's trophy with his name engraved on it; a Molson's overnight traveling bag; a $50 "student scholarship," which is presented to him by team president Gilles Gagnon; a $100 AM/FM radio and cassette-player, courtesy of one of the team's commanditaires (sponsors) *Gagnon et Frères Meubles;* and a basket of fruit – oranges, clementines, a pineapple, value $25.

It's a mark of honour in the community to sponsor the local hockey team. One enthusiastic sponsor refers to it as "the freedom of publicity." The team has five main *commanditaires.* Apart from *La Compagnie Norfruit,* which supplies the equipment and crates of oranges, and Molson's Brewery, which furnishes two cases of beer for every game, one for the directors and one for the players, and *Gagnon et Frères* furniture store, which sponsors the between-periods *lancement de la rondelle* contest, there's also *Liqueur Saguenay* providing orange drinks, 7-Ups, and Pepsis, and *l'epicerie Rond-point,* which furnishes gum, Kleenex and coffee. In addition, during the season, 20 local businesspersons will pay $200 each for the honor of sponsoring one of the team's 20 home games. For this, the game sponsor will have the name of his enterprise broadcast three times during each period over the P.A.

"We're all a little spoiled," admits one of the entrepreneurs.

First Period Summary

0:01 The puck is dropped at centre ice, directly under the Molson's clock advertising the *tabagie Métabetchouan* and *restaurant Coco-rico,* famous for its pizza and *poutine.* It's a firebrand-style of hockey; the caliber isn't as high as in the Major Junior Leagues, but the action is unabated and furious, and in the tiers of seats surrounding the *patinoire,* it's just as frenzied.

The Norfruits have their own devoted rooting section, an official fan club with at least a dozen members, led by male nurse Marc-André Dufour; throughout the game, there is the hue and cry: "Sess Sess Go Go! Go Go Sess Go!" – like a hissing snake. "Sess" is the sound of the team's initials "SS" quickly repeated over and over again. But ironically, it sounds like Cesse, from the verb cesser, to stop. Thus, the refrain can be heard as "Stop Go Stop Go Stop Go" ("Go" is the only English word ever heard in le centre sportif).

There are other idiomatic forms worth knowing if one is to enjoy hockey in Lac St-Jean: *Gros débile* (big dunce) is always a reference to the referee. *Niaiseux* (simpleton) is either the referee or an opposing player. Plante-le! or Ecrase-le! means smash him against the boards, hit him. The shout *"Pique! ... Pique!"* is used to scare an opposing player, to make him think there's a bulldozer coming at him and he'd best forget about the puck. *"Y'a perdu son cap"* means he lost his head, or cap, went haywire, most likely wanted to beat up on an opponent or the referee.

8:14 *"Mesdames et messieurs ...* " begins a message by the husky-voiced "host" of each game, ringside announcer Maurice Larouche. Probably nothing contributes more to the *ambiance* in the arena than these sponsorship plugs and announcements about raffle draws and contests, which have little to do with the action on the ice, although if a goal is scored or there's a penalty Larouche may mention it in passing.

One of the two individual sponsors for tonight's game is madame Jeannine Turcotte, who has the snack bar concession. Larouche seems to love the word "succulent" and uses it in all his publicity messages.

"Mesdames et messieurs," he begins, "why don't you mosey over to the snack bar during the intermission and try a s-succulent-t coffee or a *s-succulent-t* hot dog or a juicy *s-s-sssucculent-t* hamburger, so adroitly prepared by that *très gentille femme,* madame Jeannine Turcotte ... "

15:32 The President of Lebanon is watching the game from behind the Norfruits' bench, but he seems somewhat removed. Jean-Paul Gimaiel, owner of the clothing store in the village and the only Lebanese-Canadian hockey scout in Métabetchouan, is credited with having discovered the Nordiques' Michel Goulet, a native of nearby Péribonka, which is where Maria Chapdelaine, the heroine of Quebec's most famous novel, also played.

The big news is that Gimaiel has quit his part-time job covering the *SS* for *Le Progrès Dimanche* weekly newspaper. He was being paid peanuts, he says – $48 a week after taxes – and it just wasn't worth the effort. One wonders if he won't miss it, though. The President of Lebanon is a walking encyclopedia of Lac St-Jean hockey lore. Would he go back to Lebanon? Would he be safer there? Would he join the Falangistes?

Not likely, Gimaiel says. Anyway, he wasn't born there, although his father came from the same village, Bicfaya, as his cousin, the real President Gayamel (Gimaiel became a phonetic French-Canadian corruption of the Gayamel); emigrated to Canada in 1912, and settled in Métabetchouan, where Jean-Paul was born. Jean-Paul is a short man with a dark, Mediterranean look, and although physically not your typical French Canadian, he's been totally accepted in the hockey harems. His retirement from the newspaper job, which he held for ten years, has sent a shock wave through the community.

Intermission

While the players are slurping Sunkist oranges provided by their Norfruit sponsor in the dressing room, and the Zamboni advertising *Vos Caisses Pop* cleans up the ice, the P.A. announcer tells everyone it's time for the *moitié-moitié,* or half-half draw. Fans buy these raffle tickets for a dollar each, and the total booty is split down the middle, half going to the holder of the winning ticket, the other half to Norfruit, which uses half of their half to cover basic expenses and gives the other half of their half to minor hockey. Meanwhile, the holder of the winning ticket usually gives half of his or her half to the person attending the game with them. That's why it's called *moitié-moitié.* After the winning moitié-moitié number is announced, there's the *lancement de la rondelle* or "putting the puck through the slot" contest. A number is drawn; the holder of the lucky ticket is handed a stick and puck, stumbles onto the ice and, drilling a shot from the blueline tries to put the puck through any one of three slots in a board set up in front of the net. There's a prize of $10 if he fires it through either of the side holes and $20 for the middle slot.

But the contestant is usually too nervous to come even close and there's a volley of humorous taunts from the spectators: *"Envoie-la dans le trou, branleux!"* ("Put it though the hole, you loafer!"), a voice rings out tonight as the kid with the winning number slaps at the puck and misses by a country mile.

In her *casse-croûte,* or snack bar, madame Jeannine Turcotte is busy preparing her *succulent* hamburgers and serving Jo-Louis cakes and coffees; in the directors' room under the stands, the directors are drinking the beer so munificently provided by Molson's Brewery.

Second Period Summary

3:15 Raynald Tremblay is smiling because the Norfruits are coming on strong. Raynald is a truck driver for Norfruit, the company, and manager of Norfruit, the team. He's a Boston Bruins fan; he used to play hockey but had to give it up because of an infarctus (a type of blood circulation problem). "I've always been a *mordu de hockey*," (somebody bitten by hockey) says Raynald, who is something of a father-figure to the players, performing a variety of tasks as volunteer manager, from taping their sticks to making the team's travel arrangements.

Raynald is a member of the ubiquitous Tremblay clan. He is not related to Mario Tremblay of the Montreal Canadiens, who hails from nearby Alma and runs the *Brasserie Mario Tremblay* with Denis Tremblay, who is not related to either Mario or Raynald. Nor are any of them related to the other famous hockey player from the area, former Canadiens defenceman J.C. Tremblay of Bagotville. Monsignor Victor Tremblay wrote a history of the area that touched all bases except hockey, but he wasn't related to Mario, Raynald, J.C. or Denis. Joachim Tremblay, who built the church in Métabetchouan in 1928, wasn't related to Victor Tremblay either, although it's suspected he knew him.

A check of the Saguenay-Lac St-Jean phone book reveals that there are 20 full pages of Tremblays. There are four columns on each page and approximately 65 names in each column, or 260 Tremblays per page, times 20 pages, equals 5,200 Tremblays with phones. Say there are another 800 without phones; that comes to 6,000 Tremblay family units, times, let's say, five persons per family, or 30, 000 Tremblays, give or take a few.

In Métabetchouan, one out of every four persons is called Tremblay. You can stop anybody on the street and, playing it safe, say, "Monsieur Tremblay, where is the hockey arena?" The person may be cautious at first and inquire, "How did you know my name?" But then he'll reply, "It's about a mile out of town, on the right side of the road, monsieur Tremblay."

8:46 The Northern Fruits score, and there are three wails of a police siren, operated by the president of *La Compagnie Norfruit* and team director, Pierre Gagné, who never misses a game; there are *applaudissements,* pats on the back, shaking of hands, everything but fireworks!

11:07 The team's governor, the ex-cop, Carol Fortin, is a solid presence in the arena. He's been connected with the club since it began its Junior "AA" life ten years ago. He's a fund of information about the team, and can rattle off names of players, how many goals they had, where they are now, whether they've retired … .

Métabetchouan has its honor role of heroes. If the Montreal Canadiens have retired the Rocket's Number 9 and the Leafs have retired Teeder Kennedy's Number 7, the Norfruits have retired the Number 11 worn on the back of their former great player, Jean-Marc Chabot. He was *"un leader un gros travailleur, un joueur complet,"* says Fortin.

Legends abound, too. Many involve the ex-cop Fortin; for instance, the time he walked across the ice in the middle of a game to break up a fight in the stands. The referee didn't even blow the whistle to stop play. Another time Fortin got wind that his provincial police colleagues would be raiding a bar where the underage Norfruit players were engaged in a darts tournament. It was Fortin, in fact, who had organized the tournament. He quickly rounded up the players and drove them to his home, where the dart play continued.

And if there existed a medal-of-bravery, it would have to be awarded to the team's former trainer, Richard Pleau. The story is now part of Métabetchouan mythology. In the middle of a game, he jumped over the boards onto the ice to minister to an injured Northern Fruit. Pucks were whistling by him on all sides and bodies hurtling past as the action continued; oblivious to the danger, Pleau passed smelling salts under the player's nose, felt for broken bones, forced open his eyelids to see if he was still alive. Mothers tell this story at bedtime to their children: "The Day Richard Pleau Jumped on the Ice … "

16:23 "*Mesdames* – " Maurice Larouche wails over the P.A. system, "why waste your precious time bent over the stove, baking bread and pizza and *pâté viande,* when you can buy all these succulent delicacies, adroitly prepared for you *Chez monsieur Pierre Lajoie,* the pastry king. He welcomes all hockey fans, any day of the week, open at 11:30 every morning … "

Third Period Summary

8:15 "Now take your average zoo –" smiles the ex-mayor Charles-Emile Brassard as Tremblay smashes Fortin into the boards. Brassard, who attends every game with his wife Juliette, always watching the action from the same green corner seats, Number 437 and 438, had been Métabetchouan's mayor for 17 years until he retired last year. He's a placid man, not known for outbursts of emotion. Raynald Tremblay describes him as being "very analytical. Sometimes he even gives our coach strategic advice, but never in a critical or negative way."

Gagnon enters the fray and hammers Tremblay, who drops his gloves and takes a whack at Fortin.

"Now take your average zoo –" the ex-mayor repeats. He hardly seems aware of *les élans de rubustesse* – the ferocious action, the crunching bodychecks, the flying elbows – taking place in the corner a few feet away from him on the other side of the glass partition. Brassard, 63, has spent most of his life in Métabetchouan, but was born in nearby St-Félicien, not far from the present site of the zoo, created on an island in the Chamouchouane River.

“In most zoos in the world, the animals are in cages and the patrons circulate freely to observe the so-called *wild* life.”

Fortin isn’t happy with the treatment he is getting from Tremblay and rams Gagné into the boards; Gagné in turn cross-checks Bonneau while Plourde knocks down Gagnon and elbows one of the Tremblays.

“But in St-Félicien,” Brassard continues, calmly, hardly noticing as Simard slashes Bouchard, who knees Lapointe, “it’s quite the opposite. The visitors are in cages in a tractor-pulled train while the kangaroos and muskrats scuttle around freely.”

Gagnon and Gagné have now started to mix it up in the corner. Fortin shoves his glove in Grenier’s face and Tremblay throws a bruising bodycheck at Doré, which causes the glass to reverberate. Plourde doesn’t like that one bit and clobbers Simard. Brassard’s eyes are watery and happy as he reflects on the authenticity of the zoo in St-Félicien. His mind seems elsewhere, on safari in the dark wilderness of the central African plateau as Tremblay of the other team comes in and gores Tremblay of the first team, who doubles up in pain.

“The polar bears have a rock to themselves in the middle of the river, not far from the beaver dam.” Bonneau has just dropped his gloves and mauls the Tremblay kid who attacks Gagnon who spears Fortin who whomps the older Tremblay. “There are monkeys swinging from the trees and the mountain goats are on the hills.” Ouellet nails Villeneuve who smashes Geoffrion who garrotes Beliveau. “There’s a puma carousing through the park and the giraffes nibble the leaves off the trees.” Now Fortin decides to crunch the first Tremblay who in turn bashes Gagnon who slams Gagné. “But the best time to catch *ouananiche*,” the ex-mayor muses, “is in the spring when the ice melts and you can troll in the shallows around the mouth of the Kouspaganiche River with about 200 feet of line and a silver spoon.”

The referee finally blows the whistle; the action stops. The ice is littered with debris and bodies; there is more pushing, fighting and knocking down before order is restored.

"But the camels and gazelles in St-Félicien are caged in for the winter because of the extreme cold. I think the lions and hippos are inside as well ..."

Hot *Poele* League

The game is over; the fans are filing out. Who won? Who scored? Surprise, I'll tell you. Here it is, a little memo on the last page of my notebook marked "Peripheral events – padding to be used if necessary."

We won: 5-2. That's what it says. And now we're five points out of first place, and, yes, we even have a mathematical chance of catching *les Marquis* before the end of the season and taking the divisional title, if we stay out of the bars before the games and devote ourselves to hockey ... .

The harems of Lac St-Jean: but *after* the game, it's *la fête* – celebration. The brass and players repair to a dimly lit disco in the centre of town called *Le Bar-Ro,* "Ro" standing for the name of the former owner, Ronald. Here, at last, a chance to scout the multitudinous, pulchritudinous women of the region, who, it's said, outnumber the men four-to-one and are renowned for their beauty. Five days of macho hockey atmosphere is enough. It's time for a cursory descent into the harems of Lac St-Jean. Looking for Mr. Badbar.

But the Bar-Ro is so dark that unless you have panther-like vision, you can't see a thing. You can't even see your own hand held up in front of your face, much less the face of another person.

I've been dancing frenetically with a silhouette, no doubt a tempestuous young thing with the kind of curves you read about in detective novels, if only you could see them. She's holy and slim. Time is moving fast. When I ask her what her name is and if she'd like to join me back in my room in the Motel Terrasso for some buttered toast, she replies in a gruff voice, "I'm Tremblay, the goaltender for the Northern Fruits."

And so ends my report on the hockey harems of Lac St-Jean.

Barry Butson

Classic City Arena on Friday Nights

The cold walk to the rink,
the warm lobby where
big men in thick red coats
and women in furs are crowded
in talk and smoke, drinking
hot chocolate from paper cups
they crush with heels afterwards,
as they head in for the game.

I am merging with them quite happily
as they pass through the ticket gate,
racing up the stairs
before the ticket-taker can grab me.
Possibly he didn't care;
maybe he grinned.

Cold along the upper level walkway,
standing room only,
players circling the ice
in pre-game ritual I can't see
but can hear the blades slicing
and the pucks being slapped.
I am climbing onto the steel rafters
because there are no empty seats.

An usher may or may not order me down.
Warm by the third period,
temperatures raised by 3,000 fans,
their passion reaching the cold steel rafters
where I perch less like vulture than
one of the swifts that live in the arena's
upper reaches, back pressed against a post
legs hanging down.

Our team seldom lost
with that Roth, Flick and Flanagan line.
I had no money,
but I saw every game.

Rob Siciliano

Hockey Haiku

Indian summer
Still going strong
I hope the Habs win tonight

Toronto is my city
But it sure as hell
Ain't my hockey team

Pour moi c'est le C-H
Toujours et encore
Le Tricolore

It can't get any worse for the Leafs
They're 26th overall
There are no more teams on the league

Grievances and comments from Leaf fans
and the host of the show
Post-mortems on Talk 640

Nothing to look forward to this season
Leafs' talk: the topic of tonight's show is rebuilding
The 20-YEAR PLAN

The thirty-year Stanley Cup drought continues
The Leafs are last overall
Cliff Fletcher is a genius

The marquee at the MLG says:
"The management thanks you for enduring another season of mediocrity...
have a good summer and drive safely"

Talking Yellow Pages
Don't want to hear a psychic reading
I want to hear the hockey scores

I called the Hotline
Much to my delight
We hung on to beat the Flyers 6-5

It's getting ridiculous
Listening to Hab games on the radio
I'm even memorizing the commercials

Jesus saves but...
Pierre Turgeon
Scores on the rebound

Turgeon got traded to the Blues
Another captain gone
Mauvaise transaction

Jesus saves but...
Mark Recchi
Scores on the rebound

La Folie Des Series
Playoff hockey
Riveted to the T.V.

I won two tickets to Disney On Ice
To see the lowly Leafs versus
The Mighty Ducks Of Anaheim

The Cold War hasn't ended
It's continued
On the ice

I want to be a nutcase
Like Lyle Odelein
Rifling a puck at the Sabres' bench

Scott Beal

Two Shakespearean Madwomen Versus the 1996 Detroit Red Wings

Ophelia gazes forlornly into the polished surface of the ice,
brushing a wisp of hair behind an ear – her reflected face
  gauzy,
already covered by a thin winding sheet – she's feeling lost, it's
an omen, she's doomed to a role that ends in drowning,
but she goes on humming anyway – when Stu Grimson
  speeds by and lays on
a vicious cross-check. The crowd's subsequent lowing sounds
like booing, but rather they're invoking his name, slapping
backs, Stu, Stoooo, spilling beer. There's going to be a whistle.
  The Grim Reaper (as he's known) is going to spend the
  next two
minutes in the box. Now a face-off. The object is to control
the puck, black spot you've seen spinning from stick to stick,
  miniature void
that cruises across the field of white, portable hole running
  the gamut
of the rink. Knock it in the net to slap your foe a deficit.
Regan has a finesse for sticking men with debits. She knew
she'd be surrounded with ice and she came prepared, brought
  her
icepick, the same awl she uses to relieve her elders of their
  eyeballs.

The Red Wings ain't sissies, shuck off their faceguards. We're in
for a hell of a match. I'm in
my living room, bug-eyed inches
from the icy rink of the TV screen, an inactive participant
in the action, bug-eyed lumpish mass propped on cushions,
wrapped in patchwork.
I'm basted in white light reflected off the frost the skaters
navigate. Behind me ten-cent cans are stacked to rinse and
return, unread
classics (Seuss and Shelley) bracket Shakespeare, a cleaver
needs sharpening under the mattress. There are letters to send
to friends in Jersey, in jail, in the Senate. The black hole
of the puck skitters over me, pauses at my knee, at the bottom
of my breast pocket, Federov slides it to Primeau at my throat,
he shoots, he scores. It's a random roving acupuncture
without power
to heal, pitting me with cavities too small for bullets, more like
heated knitting needles – the tool in Regan's grip, if you care
to extend the metaphor. I don't. I'm thinking
about dramatics,
whether it's more thrilling to witness the memorized frenzy
of five acts, or the more-loosely-regulated frenzy of three (plus
overtime if necessary), the freewill or determinism
argument of hockey vs. theater. I'd like to think my inertia
isn't scripted, I could fling off this blanket, these jeans, flannel,
socks and boxers, run every red light to Champ's,
knock back some fat coveralled oaf's bourbon, hurl the
shot glass

at the bigscreen behind the bar and see if goaltender Chris
Osgood

can still preserve the shutout. But I haven't

forgotten Ophelia – she hasn't risen from that bone-churning
crash

into the boards – and what's more there's blood. It's reflected
in my

crackle-red eyes, glazed rinks sunk in my skull, with the pupils'
dark pits

centered in the face-off circle, waiting for a slapshot, a one-
timer.

Bob Wakulich

Hockey Games and Naked Ladies

Standing on the icy sidewalk, Crank could see light bleeding from the edges of Harvey's bay window curtains. He had tried to call twice, letting the phone ring a total of twenty-seven times.

He pressed a thick mitten to the stairwell door and pushed. A resident mouse ran for cover and a bare light bulb hanging from a cord at the top of the stairs began to sway, pulling shadows back and forth.

The staircase squealed and creaked with every mukluk step, Crank appearing as a green mass of moving parka with a steaming breath. At the landing, he saw a note taped to the light's pull chain: "GO AWAY." He pounded on the door.

. . .

Harvey sat in cross-legged bliss on a beanbag chair, a set of high-tech headphones drowning out reality. The floor had been shaking a little, but he'd shrugged this off to another low-flying plane waiting to land at the airport. This assumption had to be discounted when he glanced across the room and saw the corner of a plastic card wriggling its way up to the lock.

As he reached over to shut off the tape deck, the card found its mark and the door flew open, the chain-lock assembly breaking away from the door frame. Harvey's headphones pulled themselves off as he instinctively dove for the rug. Above him, a pile of library books toppled, showering down from the desktop. A rush of cold air wafted across his back.

He slowly looked over his right shoulder and saw a clump of black beard protruding from a faded green hood. "Get that skinny ass of yours in gear, Harvey! The hockey game's on!"

"For chrissakes, Crank..."

"Time's a-wasting, son!" Crank imposed himself on the room, a weighty boot coming down squarely on a pair of stray granola bars. "Playoffs, man! Seventh game of the quarter-finals!" He raised his mittens. "Goddamn game of the century!"

"So?"

He lowered his arms. "Can you spot me a twenty 'til Monday?"

"Jesus." Harvey sat up amongst the fallen texts and pointed at the stairwell light. "Can't you read?"

"Yeah, yeah, yeah. Come on, let's go!" Crank slapped his mittens together. "Get on your galoshes, son. We're going to *The Plaza*."

"I'm busy, Crank. It's freezing outside. I can't."

"Sure you can! A big, strong college boy like you, hey, no problem! Why watch midgets when *The Plaza* has a six-foot screen? It's a goddamn wonder of modern times!"

Harvey looked down at his scattered reference books, dislodged bookmarks and scribbled notes. "So what? Why the hell do I..." He caught sight of something red, his ski-jacket in mid-flight. It draped itself over his head. He pulled it away with a jerk. He watched as Crank pushed through the room, turning off the kitchen light, shutting off the amplifier, bits of snow dropping from his boots. "I can't go, Crank. I've gotta do an essay."

Crank stopped and put his mittens on what were probably his hips. "Like hell. Essays've got nothing to do with anything." He glanced over at the tape deck. "Seems to me you were taking a break anyway."

"I..." Harvey lowered his head. It was possible to talk Crank out of these things sometimes, settle him on the couch and let him cheer while furtive attempts were made to get some work done, but the bloody TV was on the fritz and there was absolutely no liquor on hand.

. . .

Harvey settled into the passenger seat of Crank's aging Toyota and tried to wring the cold from his hands. "So what's so great about The Plaza these days?"

"Strippers pulling gee-strings." Crank revved a little more life into his engine. "Shipping 'em in from the States somewhere." He put his defroster on high, put his car into gear and pulled out, the rear wheels spinning on the snow-packed road. "They've got a short blonde with incredible thighs. She grabs her ankles and reels back on a bearskin rug." Crank flipped back his hood and looked over for a reaction. Harvey tugged at a sideburn and cast a wary eye at some sloppily-parked cars.

The *Toyota* began to slide, its rear wheels suddenly deciding to try to take the lead. Crank gave the steering wheel an abrupt half-turn. "There's a harem girl, and a jungle Amazon. Quality stuff."

Harvey grabbed at his armrest and sat quietly. Near-wipeouts had become an expected minor irritation in the whole of Crank's winter driving style. When the car straightened out, Crank smiled and squirmed in his seat. Harvey crossed his arms and sighed. "What's all this crap about naked ladies? What about the hockey game?"

"You can't watch hockey all the time. If you quit looking up references once in a while, maybe you'd find out about these... Oh, Christ!"

As the *Toyota* slid sideways through a four-way stop, Harvey closed his eyes and wondered briefly about fate and divine intervention.

. . .

The red carpet in the lobby of *The Plaza Hotel* was starting to show traces of its underweave. A thin, shriveled woman was perched on a stool behind the registration desk with her nose dipped into a copy of Alfred Hitchcock's *Mystery Magazine.* Crank pulled off his mittens and threw her a salute, and she gave them a tight-lipped smile as they headed for the *Casanova Lounge.* "Somebody told me that she watches for cops," Crank muttered, unzipping his parka. "Pushes a button or something."

The bar was still only dotted with patrons, but Harvey heard a loud, obnoxious and familiar laugh through the half-darkness from somewhere near the back. "Jeez Crank, I think that's my prof."

Crank smiled. "All yer basic hoi-polloi."

"The one I'm doing the essay for. He gave me an extension."

"Well, I guess we won't be joining THAT table." Crank surveyed the room, a lop-sided ell-space with the bar counter running along the wall beside them. The stage and the giant TV screen were in the far corner. Harvey peered through the dim lighting, shadows and pockets of cigarette smoke, taking note of the waitresses and their high-cleavage German barmaid attire. "Perfect!" said Crank. "Front row centre!"

Within five minutes, they were settled in at a table near the stage working on two jugs of pale ale. The room swelled with waves of students in team jerseys, war veterans sporting their parade berets and honest working men slapping the backs of each other's company shirts. Harvey downed a glass of draught, unable to shake a pervasive ooga-booga feeling. "Who's playing, Crank?"

"The LEAFS, man. The Leafs."

"The Leafs and who?"

Crank stared at the blank TV screen. "The Islanders." He shook his head. "Just yell for the blue guys, okay?"

"Hey, Johnny!" someone yelled. "Take it off, Johnny! Take it off my tab!" Yelling and catcalls continued as a short man in classy casuals walked to centre stage and adjusted his bolo. He signalled for quiet. "I guess you're all ready!" The yelling surged. "The girls are ready too!" The crowd noise dipped. "They'll be dancing between periods and after the game." The room had almost fallen silent. "We'll be turning on the game in just a minute. Enjoy."

There were various reactions to this arrangement, but Crank seemed to speak for the majority. "Those intermission guys can really be morons sometimes anyway." He poured out another draught. "Yeah, and that idiot with his replays." He squeaked his voice. "There now, you see how he shoots that puck? He gets it right on his stick and he shoots it right in. Let's see that again. Back it up here. See there? It's right on his STICK. See that?"

. . .

The opening period proved to be a rough and tumble affair, much to the delight of those in attendance. A pushing match started in the first minute of play, and the game was barely seven minutes old when both benches cleared for a major slugfest. Harvey offered some color commentary. "Looks like a dance marathon."

Crank slapped the table when one of the linesmen fell down. "All right!" He signalled for another two jugs. There were lots of booming bodychecks and a number of pas-de-deux's, but it was still a scoreless tie after twenty minutes.

A chorus of moans rose when the screen went white, but wolf whistles filtered through when the short blonde dancer bubbled onto the stage. Ragtime music bellowed out from woofers and tweeters as she unrolled a fake fur rug, peeled away a flimsy negligee and began her session. The crowd applauded and cheered as she jiggled and jostled away her gee-string. Harvey spilled some beer into his lap. The crowd yelled out for more.

In what turned out to be the finale, she went into her standard backreel. Crank pointed and squeaked his voice again. "See the way she moves her ankles there? Let's see that again. Take that back. There, see those ANKLES?"

When the music stopped, there was a burst of applause as the blonde stood up, bowed and started to gather her props. The TV came back on just as the puck was being dropped at centre ice, and the patrons cheered the perfect timing.

Both teams started out the second period short-handed, which seemed to put a damper on the dropping of gloves. When the Islanders scored, many in the room were certain that it was offside, and when they scored again a minute later, the major complaint was a high stick. Crank took a large swallow from his glass. "Goddamn Leafs. I got five bucks on this."

"That dancer was great." Harvey's look was distant.

"The what?"

The Leafs scored on a deflection from the point. All the heads in the room rose half a foot. Crank began to pound the tabletop, and others joined in.

The Leafs were still behind when the period ended. Patrons piled into the lounge washroom and the waitresses were backlogged with requests. There was sitar music coming from the woofers and tweeters as the second stripper busied herself with an economy version of The Dance of a Thousand Veils.

Crank, an old hand at bypassing restroom traffic tie-ups, headed for the hotel tavern facility. Harvey had already taken a break during the period, and he happily counted scarves until he heard a familiar voice moving towards him. "Down in front! I can't see the dancer!"

Before long, the inebriated but scholarly presence of Doctor Mitchell was leaning heavily into his table. "Excuse me." He was a little shaky and out of breath. "Do you mind if I sit here for a minute? All these people insist on standing up to discuss power plays. Is it all right if I..."

Harvey turned, and the two exchanged pie-eyed stares. "How are you, Professor?"

Doctor Mitchell eased into Crank's chair. "I'd be fine if I could see. Terrible planning." He watched a scarf fall to the stage. "Tell me something, Dadich."

"What's that, sir?"

"Do you always get snowstorms in late April here? I thought things were bad enough in Oregon."

"We get a big storm every year. Sometimes we get a hailstorm in June, too."

"Horrible business. You'd think it would keep these people at home."

"It's the hockey game, sir."

“Ah, yes.” Another scarf fell. “It’s almost like the Romans, you know. The Christians and the lions, the coliseums.”

“Yes sir.”

“Are you cheering for anyone, Dadich?”

Another scarf. “Pardon, sir?”

Doctor Mitchell stood up. “The hockey game, man. Which team are you yelling at?”

“Oh, the Leafs, sir. The blue guys.”

“Yes, I’ll try that.” He looked at the dancer. “See if you can get me a scarf, Dadich. I really should get back.” Doctor Mitchell swayed a little, squeezed between two tables and tottered away.

The third period was two minutes old when the TV came back on. No one had scored, but a fight had just ended and two players were shown heading for their dressing rooms. The crowd yelled in disapproval. Someone at the back told everyone to SHUTTUP. A spotlight came on behind the bar. A policeman walked in.

When the Leafs tucked in the tying goal on a drop pass, Harvey had to duck to avoid a number of flailing arms. The policeman left. The spotlight went off.

As the period wore on, Harvey noticed that more and more patrons took on glassy-eyed stares. Even Crank had drifted away, his attention nailed to the screen, his hand holding tight on his draught glass, which Harvey refilled whenever he topped off his own.

With five seconds left in the game, the Islanders drew a penalty for interference, which prompted a face-off in their defensive zone. The Leafs pulled their goaltender and a great many patrons wrung their hands.

A shot from the point bounced off the Islander goalie and bounced around crazily in front of the net. Everybody in the room stood up.

Players were poking, prodding, falling. People at the back of the bar began to wail. "Come on! Come ON!" yelled Crank.

An Islander defenseman fell on the puck like a soldier trying to smother a live grenade. The horn sounded and the patrons collectively sunk back into their seats. Someone called for a penalty shot. Crank mopped some sweat away from his forehead and waved for the waitress. "Whoa! Well, I always did like Sudden Death."

. . .

Halfway through a beer commercial, the screen went white and Johnny reappeared on stage. "We're gonna have another girl on in just a minute, folks."

Crank, his glass raised to his lips, froze. "What?"

"As soon as she's done her thing, we'll get back to the game, okay?" A long, melodic raspberry resounded throughout the room.

Harvey could see scowls forming on a number of faces, including Crank's. "This woman dances forever. She's gonna dance right into the overtime. We're gonna miss it."

"Maybe she'll do a short set," said Harvey.

"Like hell. It takes her ten minutes to set up."

It was at least another three minutes before the dancer appeared and began to arrange a collection of large stuffed animals on the stage to the beat of drums. She feigned attacks from a few of them. Some patrons laughed, while others looked at their watches.

When the menagerie had been arranged just so, she started to move and gyrate around them, dancing through the first few minutes in a relative calm, slowly stripping away pieces of loincloth. "Hurry it up!" someone yelled. There was laughter, and the room began to fill with heckles.

The dancer looked perplexed, but kept on, carefully and tantalizingly pulling away each piece. She managed to raise a few cheers when she picked up a chrome rod and did a mock limbo, but when she finally pulled away the last slice of loincloth and raised her arms, someone yelled, "Okay! Back to the game already!"

The dancer went down on her hands and knees and did a pelvic tilt in time with the beat. She caught sight of Crank staring at her in an apparent trance. She leaned way over and blew him a kiss.

Crank flapped his hand. "Go dance outside!" The yelling and heckles became a frenzied drone.

Crank slammed his draught glass on the table. "That guy is dumber than a sack of hoe handles!" He stood up and stomped towards Johnny. Harvey could see the dancer's look of confusion growing. He sighed.

. . .

Crank leaned over the bar. Johnny straightened his bolo. They both showed off their best phony smiles. "Maybe you should give the people what they want, pal."

"We pay the girls to dance," said Johnny, "and that's what they're going to do. If you don't like it, go someplace else."

"I really don't think you understand the gravity of the situation, friend." Crank pointed at the ceiling. "You don't want to end up with a lounge under the stars, do you?"

Johnny straightened his bolo again. "It's my place, my TV. We pay the girls to dance." A couple of draught glasses broke against a wall. Crank continued to point.

. . .

The jungle drums stopped with the dancer in mid-thrust. The room exploded in applause, which continued until the screen lit up to reveal the teams shaking hands at centre ice.

The dancer, feeling exposed by the lack of music, grabbed at pieces of loincloth and tried to cover up. "You people are sick!" she yelled.

The patrons remained silent as they sat and watched the replay. The dancer continued to yell. "You bunch of hicks!"

"Let's see that again now."

"You ignorant bastards!"

"He just let it go from the blue line there."

"What kind of men are you?"

"You kids out there, see that?"

Crank came back to the table and grabbed his parka. "Let's go someplace else, Harvey. ANYplace else." The dancer was still yelling, but stopped when Crank looked up and pointed at her. "Don't you understand? You are a pleasant DIVERSION, lady! A DIVERSION! That's all! THAT," he said, pointing to the screen, "that is a VOCATION!"

. . .

The following Monday afternoon, Harvey handed Doctor Mitchell an essay about societal influences on contemporary communication policies. It included a section of loosely-related field research. The paper was wrapped in a white silk scarf.

Sue Ellen Thompson

Watching the Stanley Cup Finals

Glued to the tube like all the other fools
who hunker in darkened rooms tonight,
faces glazed with blue uncertain light,
I know nothing of the game, its labyrinth of rules

or the geometric track laid by the puck that slices
diagonally across my television screen.
Still, here I am, propped up by caffeine
and pillows while someone checks and someone ices

and the crowd chants Something Something Rangers
to the boistering of an organ. My mother, a fan
so ardent she once entered the no-man's land
known to us as "The Rotten Apple," brazening the dangers

of Madison Square Garden, to see her boys
beat back the Devils, cannot be here
to see them slash their way through the ionosphere
of hockey history. In Pennsylvania, the only noise

in the crowded parlor of the funeral home
is the murmur grief makes when death
is not sudden but sadly overtime, and etiquette
dictates an end to the game. My phone

rings in the second period. She comes right
to the point: What's the score? A short pass
down the corridor, her neighbor's husband basks,
oblivious to the hugeness of her sacrifice,

in cleverly positioned tracklight, looking better
everyone agrees, than he did in life.
It's two to one, the Rangers, and the wife
of the deceased – my mother's neighbor, bless her –

weeps copiously in gratitude
for the remaining population of her world
but knows it's not enough. The Canucks hurl
one into the post. My mother eschews

the buffet afterward, and giving the widow a firm
if moist embrace, she and my father hit the road.
The game is nearly over, an episode
already largely consigned to videotape, but the third

period, as she well knows, can change
everything. Leaving death behind, they drive
back toward New England, toward life,
at ninety miles an hour. I've got a champagne

bottle chilling in the freezer. I'm prepared
to celebrate or grieve, as she would,
with a passion I didn't think I could
inherit at this late date, having never shared

her lust for men with blood on their teeth
and ridgelines in their noses, men with French
Canadian names and gutturals, hair drenched
in the chill sweat of the arena, but I believe

they're more than that to her, more
than the youth and strength they wear
as lightly as a jersey. Suddenly I cannot bear
their losing. If I've scorned the sport

in the past, I embrace it now with fists
and grimaces, with eyes cast heavenward then back
to where my mother's team swirls in an abstract
fast-forward waltz and, in a moment the columnists

will be dissecting for weeks to come, wins.
Now I'm the one who weeps and cheers
as she would have, had she been here
to signify the country of my origins.

Edo van Belkom

Hockey's Night in Canada

The first thing that impressed him was the colour of the seats. When he'd watched games on television as a kid they were always filled with people, but now that they were empty the gold and the red and the blue and the green all seemed to have a magical glow to them.

Maple Leaf Gardens.

More than just an arena, it was a shrine, a temple to the great game that Canada had given to the world.

"Hey Wilson!" came the voice of Leaf coach Reg Chase. "Get them stars outta your eyes and get on the ice!"

Kevin Wilson looked over at Coach Chase and nodded. Then he took a deep breath and stepped onto the pristine sheet of Gardens' ice. At first his knees felt a little weak, but after a few strides the nervous tension he'd been feeling all morning finally began to subside.

It was time to get down to business. And that business was making the Toronto Maple Leafs line-up.

Wilson actually had a decent shot at earning himself a spot on the team. The young defenseman from Brampton had been a second-round draft pick and was coming off a stellar year with the Ontario Hockey League's Ottawa 67s. He stood six feet tall, weighed in at just over two-hundred pounds, and according to what had been written in a few of the Toronto papers, was just what the Leafs needed to help them make a serious run at Lord Stanley's Cup.

But realistically speaking, there was only one spot open on defense and two candidates for the job. Wilson was one, the other was a highly-touted Russian teenager named Boris Smolnikov.

Smolnikov was a classic Russian hockey player, much smaller than Wilson, but good with the puck and quick on his skates. It would all come down to what kind of defensemen Coach Chase thought he needed to round out the team – a rugged stay-at-home type, or an eggs-in-his-pocket, fancy-skating playmaker.

Coach Chase blew his whistle once, signaling the players to skate hard until the next whistle sounded.

Wilson put his head down and picked up speed. When he looked up he could see Smolnikov rounding the goal and made the extra effort to catch up to him.

The whistle blew again, and the players all relaxed, gliding around the rink until the time when they'd have to go hard again.

Wilson came up behind Smolnikov, and matched the Russian's speed. The next time the whistle went, they'd be side-by-side and Coach Chase would be able to make a direct comparison between the two.

The whistle blew and both players took off. Smolnikov jumped out ahead, but Wilson's stronger strides soon had him caught up to his rival. Then as they approached the end boards, Wilson drifted slightly right, cutting off Smolnikov's lane and forcing him to slow down to make the turn around the goal. When they came out the other side, Wilson was a good dozen feet in front.

The whistle blew once more and Wilson glanced over at Coach Chase. Unfortunately, the man had been looking the other way, but Wilson knew there were still plenty of assistants and scouts up in the stands. They were watching the two players closely too, comparing them against each other every step of the way.

The session moved on to a one-on-one drill that pit each defenseman against a single forward – the forward's objective being to score, the defenseman's job being to stop him, or at least prevent him from getting a decent shot on goal.

Smolnikov's first test came at the hands of Dimitri Litovsk, the Leafs' top scorer and perennial all-star. As Litovsk came down the ice, Smolnikov neatly poke-checked the puck off his stick, ending the rush.

Somehow, it all looked too easy to Wilson. Litovsk could have skated circles around Smolnikov if he'd wanted to, but instead he'd lost the puck like some kid out of Junior.

When Wilson's turn came up, he was pitted against Roy Baxter, a tough-guy fighting for his own spot on the team. Baxter was a decent puckhandler, but a little slow on his skates and Wilson was able to ride him to the boards without a shot being taken.

Smolnikov's next opponent was a Vladimir Karkhov, a third-line centre and penalty-killing specialist. Again, Smolnikov was able to easily poke the puck off Karkhov's stick.

There was something funny going on, thought Wilson, and he had to do something about it.

There were two defenseman before him in line, but he said, "Let me take this one," and headed out to face the next forward up, Dimitri Litovsk. Suddenly the high-scoring Russian had all kinds of speed and his head was faking left and right as if he was in some overtime playoff game. Wilson ignored the head movements and stayed with the man, lining him up for a check.

And then his opportunity came.

Litovsk lost the puck in his skates, and put his head down for a moment to try and find it.

Wilson dug in his skates and put a shoulder into Litovsk's chest. There was a loud "Pop!" as the two made contact, and when it was over, Litovsk was flat on his back with Wilson standing over him – a big grin on his face.

A few of the players – mostly the Canadians – whooped it up, or slapped their sticks on the ice.

"All right, all right," shouted Coach Chase, as he skated over to Litovsk. "Take five, everybody."

Wilson, savoring the moment, slowly skated over to a group of defensemen taking a drink of water by the boards.

"Nice check!" said Wayne Devereaux, a veteran blueliner with four years with the Leafs and eight in the league. "Hope it helps your chances."

"What are you talking about?" said Wilson. "I just laid out the team's top scorer, that's got to count for something."

Devereaux shrugged. "Maybe, but my guess is they've already made their decision. You've either made the team or you haven't."

"You think they're going to take Smolnikov over me?"

"He's a Russian, ain't he?"

Wilson leaned against the boards, closed his eyes and let out a long sigh.

Smolnikov was Russian.

And he was Canadian.

It was one of the few things in Smolnikov's favor, but it was a big thing – if not the thing that would ultimately determine which of the two made the team.

Although Coach Chase hailed from Medicine Hat and was as Canadian as a Loonie, he was under a lot of pressure from the team's owners and management to not only put together a winning hockey team, but a winning hockey team with the right mix of players.

And that meant plenty of Russians.

There were already seven Canadians on the team, two over the mandatory league minimum, so Chase was free to choose whichever player he wanted. So what it might end up coming down to is what the fans wanted most.

And even that spelled trouble for Wilson.

The regular Saturday night broadcast of Hockey Night in Canada earned more revenue on the sale of Russian rights than it did on the sale of Canadian rights.

And then there was Victor Tikhonov and his "Coach's Corner." A half dozen times last year the garrulous former Russian coach had done segments on Smolnikov, saying he might be the best defenseman Russia has ever produced, even going so far as mentioning the name Orr in the same breath as Smolnikov. With that kind of build-up, the Russian fans probably wouldn't look kindly on the Leafs if Smolnikov didn't make the team. And that meant that Toronto's games could end up being Saturday night's secondary local broadcast.

Sure, Wilson had led the OHL in scoring by a defenseman, and topped the league in the plus-minus category, but he was a Canadian boy, and that would always be a knock against him.

Wilson looked over to the centre of the ice where Litovsk was slowly getting back onto his skates. He looked a little groggy and would likely miss the rest of the session.

"All right," shouted Coach Chase. "Split up for a scrimmage."

"Good," muttered Wilson under his breath. If there was one way to show how much better he was than Smolnikov, it was under the simulated game-type conditions of a scrimmage. He'd done well in them so far, scoring goals and throwing good checks in almost every one. Now that they'd moved training camp into the Gardens, he was sure he could make the kind of impact that would earn him a spot on the team.

When the players split into two squads, Wilson made sure Smolnikov was on the opposing team. Since they were both defensemen, they likely wouldn't be going up against each other one-on-one, but considering how much Smolnikov loved to rush with the puck there was always a chance.

Wilson started out on the bench, keenly watching the action on the ice as Smolnikov took up a position on the blueline. As he made a quick check of the rest of players on the ice, Wilson realized that all of them were Russians, every last one of them, including both goaltenders. It wasn't a good sign since the Russians were notorious for looking out for each other both on and off the ice. The rumor going around was that Litovsk had been boarding Smolnikov in his home and was driving him around town helping the kid find a house of his own.

When the puck was dropped Litovsk won the face-off, drawing it back past his two defensemen and into the corner. Smolnikov skated back for the puck, picked it up behind the net and waited for his teammates to regroup. When they were all in position, he rushed up ice, across centre and over the blueline. In the opposing team's zone, he split the defense and ended up scoring a goal on the netminder's usually strong glove-hand side.

Several players cheered, but Wilson just shook his head. He couldn't be sure if Smolnikov was so good he could skate through an entire team, or if the rest of the Russians wanted him on the Leafs roster desperately enough to look bad for the sake of their comrade. Either way it didn't look good for Wilson.

Nevertheless, he still had a chance to make the team and he was more than willing to give it his best shot. After all, what did he have to lose.

So when Wilson's shift came, he was eager to do some damage. Every time a winger got between him and the boards, he rode him out, making sure he hit the boards hard. The Canadian players didn't seem to mind the rough play so much, but the Russians started to shy away from Wilson's side of the ice, opting to head down the middle or the opposite wing to avoid getting hit.

With the opportunity to play a more physical game taken away from him, Wilson wound up with the puck on his stick more often. While he'd been a good rushing defenseman in Junior hockey, he decided to play it safe in training camp by shooting the puck high off the glass and out of trouble. It was one of those basics he'd learned in minor hockey, and it seemed to be serving him well now that he was trying to make the pros.

But the more Wilson played a stay-at-home type of defense, the more Smolnikov rushed up ice. Funny thing was that the Russian never made a rush when Wilson was on the ice, only when other Russians were defending. As a result, he managed to score another goal and assist on a third.

On Wilson's next shift, he decided it was time for him to show that he could handle the puck too. After taking a clearing pass from the goaltender at his own blueline, Wilson rushed up ice. When he realized that the defenseman standing between himself and the goalie was none other than Boris Smolnikov, he put his shoulders down and skated harder toward him.

As he had hoped, Smolnikov was caught flatfooted. Wilson's shoulder slammed into the Russian, knocking him on his rear. Still with the puck, Wilson walked in on the goalie, holding off shooting until the very last second. The goaltender, another Russian named Igor Bokachev, must have been afraid that Wilson was going to run him over because he practically moved out of the way, leaving Wilson more than half the net to shoot at.

Wilson took a shot, and Wilson scored.

The Canadians on the ice and on the bench – even the ones playing against Wilson – cheered, as did a few reporters watching the scrimmage from the stands.

With the goal, Wilson was satisfied he'd done everything he could to show that he belonged in the NHL as a member of the Toronto Maple Leafs. The rest would be up to Coach Chase and his assistants.

When the scrimmage ended, most of the players showered, changed into their street clothes and headed out for a bite to eat before the afternoon session. But Wilson stayed behind, eating a few sandwiches they'd brought into the dressing room and spending the rest of his time in the exercise room lifting weights.

According to the chart on the wall, Wilson was second on the team in the bench press. He'd have a long way to go before he could match Roy Baxter – by far the strongest man on the team – but he was a good one-hundred and fifty pounds better than Smolnikov's best effort. If he worked at it hard enough, maybe he'd be able to pump up the difference between their lifts to one-seventy-five, maybe even one-eighty.

When he was done with the weights, Wilson went over to the row of stationary bikes to get in a few miles before the afternoon session started. As he was about to set the tension on his bike, the door to the exercise room opened to reveal Coach Chase standing in the doorway.

"Wilson," he said with a flick of his head. "Can I see you in my office a minute."

"Sure, coach."

Wilson got off the bike and followed Coach Chase into his office. It was a surprisingly small office for a coach in the NHL, but it was all Chase seemed to need. There were all sorts of old photos on the walls of Leaf teams from the fifties and sixties, many of them featuring the team captain holding the Stanley Cup triumphantly over his head.

None of those photos were in colour.

"What's up coach?" said Wilson, making himself comfortable in a chair. He had an idea that he'd been called in to be told that he'd made the team. After all, the morning's performance should have been more than enough to prove that he deserved a spot on the roster more than Smolnikov did. This was it. The point he'd worked all his life to get to, his life-long dream about to be realized. He was going to remember this moment and savour it for all time.

"You followed our team last year, didn't you?"

"I'd been drafted by Toronto the year before, so yeah I kept up with whatever was written in the papers."

"Good, good," said Coach Chase. "Then you know that our defense had the third-best plus-minus rating, and allowed the fourth fewest goals in the league."

"Sure, those were good numbers."

Chase nodded. "So you realize that I've already got five good defensemen and it would be difficult for someone new to fit in with the defensive system that's already in place."

Wilson's soaring hopes suddenly came crashing down in flames. He knew that when Coach Chase said someone new, what he was really saying was a Canadian. So he wasn't going to make the team, after all. Wilson shifted uncomfortably in his seat, and placed a hand over his suddenly turbulent stomach.

"You know how it is," said Coach Chase, sounding more apologetic than authoritative. "People want to see the Russians play, they think their style of hockey's more exciting, more entertaining."

Wilson said nothing.

Chase got up and started pacing around the room. "I don't like it any more than you do, but that's the way it is. Maybe if Henderson hadn't hit the post in the dying seconds of that final game back in 1972, then maybe things would have been different. If he'd scored and we'd won the series, then maybe the Russians would have had to learn the game from us instead of the other way around. But no, he hit the post and they came back up the ice and scored..."

Chase shrugged. "The next season every team's got an operative behind the iron curtain. First Tretiak defects, then Kharlamov and Yakushev. Next thing you know, the Russians are making the deals themselves, using our money to make their hockey program stronger." Chase shook his head in dismay. "But what am I telling you all this for, kid? You probably know it as well as anybody..."

Chase sat down in the chair behind his desk. "Look, I'd love to stack the team with Canadian talent, play it tough, you know, real old-time hockey, but the owners want a team full of Russians. Better for product licensing and television revenue. I almost convinced them to start building up a team with young Canadian talent, but the Canucks shot that all to hell last spring when they won the Cup by dressing every Russian on the roster through the playoffs."

Chase suddenly threw up his hands as if he were disgusted by the whole situation.

Wilson took a deep breath and nodded. Who'd he been trying to kid? Who'd want a Canadian defenseman when they could have one of the best young Russians instead?

But, he reasoned, maybe things might change. If the Leafs couldn't use him, then maybe another team could. There was talk about the Oilers making the move to strictly homegrown talent. Sure it was a cost-saving measure on their part, but it was still a chance to play in the bigs.

Wilson decided he'd work twice as hard this year and be ready if and when the call came.

"Am I going back to junior?" he asked.

Chase shook his head. "No, we don't think another year in junior as an over-age is going to help you much. We're sending you off to our minor league affiliate in Minsk."

"Really?" asked Wilson. This was good news, very good news. The Minsk Maple Leafs were one of the top teams in the Russian Hockey League, the best minor-pro league in the world. Heck, Gretzky and Lemieux were even playing out their careers there.

"Yeah, really. You'd do well there and maybe we'll call you back by mid-season."

Wilson's hopes soared once more.

They weren't giving up on him. So, he wouldn't be playing for the Leafs this year; at least he was being given the chance to improve his game by learning from the best hockey players in the world.

The Russians would teach him to play the game their way and he'd be that much better for it. Then, he'd be back in Toronto, wearing that eye-catching, army-red and white jersey the Leafs had adopted a few years ago to make them look more Russian.

The dream was not over.

Not by a long shot.

Lorna Blake

Power Play

I don't recognize the heroes reveling here –
though my son's card collection contains statistics,
photos, data he's memorized in minute detail –
or the game's appeal, aspects of it look so grim:
heads in plastic helmets, haunches padded to protect
against slamming bodies and angry slashing sticks.
But these armed gladiators glide back and forth like
so many Gretzkys on steel, with startling grace.

We're here at the Garden guzzling cokes, hot dogs while
beer-soaked fans listen to loudspeakers blaring facts,
strobe lights scatter visions and sound stabs through the roof,
blasting through space, so even the stars can stare down
at the Rangers and Devils as they duel on, red, white
and blue jerseys colliding, crushed by the boards
in the bright-lit oval. Blades scissor, carving and
stinging the ice; sticks split air into cold slices
with weapon-like zeal – more work for the Zamboni
lumbering like a tank, locked in tight
circles making its own sad, concentric maze
as it trundles around the teeming arena,
till the next punishing period; penalty calls
and whistles for hooking, icing, and high sticking
while the armored goalie guards the mouth of the cave.
What new war game is this, wonder the older gods?

Richard Harrison

Stanley Cup

At the centre of the circle of the Champions of the
World, Mario Lemieux hoists the Cup, kisses its silver
thigh, the names of men where his will soon be cut
with a finish pure as a mirror; around him, the
tumult. And Scotty Bowman, the winningest coach
in the NHL, named his first son Stanley when his
Canadiens won it in '73 with a stonewall blueline and
a dizzying transition game. Every player on every
team who ever won the Cup gets to take it home; it
has partied on front lawns, swimming pools and in
the trunks of cars, and even the man who left it on
the side of the road and drove away, still he thinks
of it as holy. And that word – holy – appears most
in the conversation of veterans who know how the
touch fades, the shoulder takes longer between days
of easy movement, how Bobby Hull passed over his
chance to drink champagne from its lip when the
Hawks won it in '61 because he thought there'd be so
many in his life. Some take the Cup apart, clean the
rings, make minor repairs in their basements, and
then inscribe on the inside of the column the un-
official log of their intimate knowledge: This way
I have loved you.

Tom Brand

The Glass-Eyed Winger

There was no "down" from the Laramie Firebirds, so it was becoming evident that I was near the end of the line. In December, they paired me up on defense with a weak-skating, chain-smoker named José whose slapshot was even worse than mine. I was thirteen years older and about fifty pounds heavier than José, but at least I knew how to clear the puck. The only guy even near my age was one of the goalies; but like half the guys on the team, he had a serious drinking problem.

Nobody respectable wants to travel to Laramie to play on an outdoor rink at 7200 feet, so we spent a lot of time on the road. We'd drive all night to play the Boise Blades who would promise us gas money just so they could end a losing streak. We always did a better job of holding up our side of the bargain than they did.

The next weekend, we'd drive up to Colorado Springs where a drunken crowd would douse us with beer at the end of the third period. Then they'd loan us three of their subs to make the Sunday game more interesting for the fans. We would give the subs the only uniforms that didn't smell like stale beer, but we'd still get thrashed.

That's not to say we didn't have a great time. Hockey players seek out a good time, and if they don't find it in a place like Salt Lake, they create it. And when they do find it in a place like Steamboat Springs, they improve it. There are men in this world who grow up wanting to be hard-working husbands with stable white-collar jobs and annual family vacations to Orlando or Maui. These are not the sort of guys who play senior town team hockey until they are almost forty.

"I seen your boy," the goalie tells me one Saturday. "If your wife keeps dressing him up in those pansy clothes, he'll have to know how to fight."

For hockey players, life is basically a fight. I knew it. My wife knew it. Although she had tried to steer me towards tennis or even skiing, she tolerated hockey. She knew there wasn't much else for someone like me to do in Wyoming.

I shouldn't stereotype all hockey players but there are some things you can count on. Wingers, for instance, always live on the edge. Always. A winger will drink a belly full of beer, latch onto a blonde in a bar, lead her back to the room to do doggy tricks with her right there in front of God and everyone and then head right back to the bar for more. Next morning, he'll smile that crooked, toothless winger smile when told what he did. Wingers are guys with short memories and even shorter fuses.

Centers are like wings – just more solitary – especially when they drink. And because they don't take care of themselves, the rest of us have to. Centers were pampered as kids – because in some previous life they were stars. But by the time they become Firebirds, there aren't any parents anymore – or coaches, for that matter. So a hung-over center will score three breakaway goals and then vomit off in the corner after every shift. When you ask what's wrong, he'll claim altitude sickness.

Defensemen like me live on the periphery, scoring fewer goals and drinking less beer. We're loners, probably because the others don't find us any more interesting than we find each other. For us, good road entertainment is a novel or a decent movie when you can find one. Occasionally you find a defenseman who wants to be in the middle of everything, but you'll also notice he likes to score goals a little too much. I guess it's a lifestyle decision.

It's harder to generalize about goalies. One goalie seemed just about like the rest of us until some hooker appeared behind the goal during the game holding a fistful of his clothes and hollering drunkenly about broken promises. Maybe it's the pressure of having to stop all those pucks.

The other goalie woke up early to go to mass as part of a thirty step ritual he always completed before a Sunday game. It's not that religion is bad for a hockey player, mind you, but the big thing is how a guy retaliates after a hard check or whether he would punch someone out in the corner. You have to be a hockey player to appreciate the nuances, I guess. Which brings me at last to the story of the glass-eyed winger.

In the West, all road trips are long so hockey players tell a lot of stories. There are the usual bar stories or woman stories, but mostly hockey stories. By the time you descend to the level of the Firebirds, you have a lot of stories about the so-called "legends." And I don't mean media creations like Gretzky or Hull, but those great marginal geniuses of hockey like the wandering goalie "Lefty" Curran or the great Indian player, Henry Boucha who tore up the NHL until he was speared in the eye by some gutless twerp. But he's not the glass-eyed winger either.

The glass-eyed winger was one of those guys who could have been great except for a sad twist of fate. Hockey lore is full of them. His story begins, like so many hockey legends, in Northern Minnesota. He was a gifted player, a flashy kid they were already calling The Next Something or Another. He even had a hockey player's name, Richard Bertrand. And as he passed through the ranks, he attracted those hero-hungry crowds who just want to see the next legend in the making.

Hockey players aren't like basketball players who get a growth spurt and suddenly arrive on the scene or football players who bulk up on steroids to get drafted by the pros. Hockey players are born great. And when a great one is born, word of it literally ripples through those great hotbeds of the northern tier of the US and Canada. Richard Bertrand was clearly one of those guys.

In the third period of a game where he had already scored a pure hat trick, young Bertrand – he was all of thirteen and hadn't even had his growth spurt – came down his right wing with a puck that danced on the ice like butter on a hot griddle. Like all great players, the kid had the knack with his stick. And he had great, fluid moves. But just as he did his patented feint into the middle, a backchecking centerman anticipated the move and sent him sprawling onto the ice. Bertrand slid on his back toward a plodding defenseman who was so focused on the puck that he apparently didn't even see him until his razor-sharp CCM sliced into the winger's face. Actually, right into his eyeball. I could described how it looked, but I usually don't. It's sickening enough without the gore.

Before face masks, incidents like this were a rite of passage, little deaths that were eventually mastered. Most of us caught a puck or stick in the face at some point – losing teeth or earning a scar – but this was clearly more serious. The boy had scarcely stopped sliding when his father vaulted over the boards and sprinted across the ice. He cradled Bertrand in his arms while they desperately waited for some doctor or a nurse to emerge from the crowd. None did, so the father picked up the boy – skates, gloves, and everything – and carried him out of the arena to his car in the parking lot and drove the 98 miles to the nearest regional hospital while the son lay whimpering in the back seat.

Long story short, the father made it there in 58 minutes but Richard Bertrand lost his eye anyway. And once a player loses an eye, he can kiss his career good-bye: no college scholarships, no Olympics, no NHL. And once he loses his hockey career, he is just as worthless as any other kid in any of those small factory towns up north. Maybe even more worthless because of what might have been.

I ran into him once a couple years later. To me, the new eye looked as realistic as the old one. I told him that, but I noticed how he looked at me incredulously with his head cocked to the side. Then I never saw him again. The father turned out to be one of those closet alcoholics whose declining health and appearance marked him as just another hourly mill worker whose son could have been a legendary hockey player. His enduring claim to fame was the fifty-eight minute flight up Highway 53.

That was the story I told, enhancing it to fit the occasion but always bringing in the essential details. Once, a center had vomited into a garbage can as I described the cold, razor-sharp blade cutting into the eyeball until it hit bone.

. . .

Well, near the end of the season, we drove across Wyoming to a truly god-forsaken place called Rock Springs. Their town team, the Rattlers, had gone through its inaugural season without winning a game in their new civic arena and someone figured we were their last great chance. There would be a game the first night and a matinee on Saturday.

So we all got off work early and drove the interstate to western Wyoming. After they fed us a spaghetti dinner in the new motel, we drove over to the arena expecting the usual humiliation. But on this night, the Firebirds played their finest game of the season. By now, José was gone and I was paired with a guy we called the Episcopalian. The idea was that I would "stay home" while he launched his creative and passionate end-to-end runs. It seemed to be working. He scored a first period goal and I was using the one skill that still remained: checking. "The hands," said one old hockey player, "are the last thing to go." I still had my hands and occasionally my body.

So, as the Rattler forwards mounted rush after rush, I enjoyed one of those magical nights when every trick I knew worked. Once during a face-off, the Episcopalian skated over to say: "Hit that jerk with the red helmet extra hard. He's slashed at me every time I've gone by."

I hadn't even noticed the guy until then, but on the next shift he carried the puck over the red line with his head down. So I leveled him. Not just once or even twice, but half a dozen times before the night was over. It was as though he chose to ignore me until it was too late. At some point, someone must have said something because soon he was slashing at my calves too. Rock Springs fans, hoping for a brawl, egged both of us on, but neither of us dropped the gloves. We pulled ahead in the third period and won, 4-3.

Because they often share the same set of interests – boasting and drinking – hockey players fraternize after games. So we all went to the post-game party in some Wild West lounge. I was sipping something cold when the woman who arrived with the red helmeted winger, probably looking for someone sober to talk to, came over to me:

"Good game," she said. "I bet you're not originally from Laramie either, are you?" I couldn't tell if she was flirting or trying to make conversation.

"Minnesota," I answered.

"That's what I figured. Me too." She was unnaturally talkative, the way Minnesotans get when they find themselves in places like Rock Springs.

"What town? I detect a little northern accent," I said.

"Littlefork," she answered. "At least, that's where I went to school." She was hoping I might be from the north also.

"Then you must have known Johnny Tremble," I said.

"He was my history teacher. How do you know him?"

"The usual," I answered, "School. We were teammates. That sort of thing." By that time, the jealous winger had moved over and, as he looked me in the eye, he cocked his head like someone who has had too much to drink and asked: "Who the hell are you, anyway? If you know Johnny Tremble, then I must know you."

When I named myself, his recognition light went on. *I was older. I was heavier. I wore a thick mustache. How had I gotten to Wyoming? Did I ever see Tremble? Shame about his divorce.*

Now it was my turn: "Who are you?"

"You wouldn't know me. You knew my brothers, the Bertrands."

"You're the...my god. Richard, right? I never dreamed I would ever see you play hockey. Not after...." I was trying to make the connection between this grizzled and gaunt-faced man and the boy of my memory when the Episcopalian had sidled over and I introduced him. "You know the guy in the story about the eye...? He's the one you asked me to flatten, the guy in the red helmet."

. . .

As we talked, Bertrand told me about a year in prison and then starting over in Rock Springs. He had married a girl from home and they had two kids. He loved Wyoming. It had given him a new chance at life – even hockey. What I was hearing was optimistic – a story of new beginnings, but only the glass eye agreed with the words. The other eye was depthless, desperate. He was telling the story for her sake; I knew the routine. My story wasn't as dramatic – school, then work, then school again. I told him I was thinking of heading back to Minnesota. Wyoming hadn't turned out the way I hoped it would.

Next morning, as we laced on our skates, the Episcopalian related the experience: "You know that story he always tells about the eyeball? It 's true. The guy with the red helmet is the glass-eyed winger." Over in the corner, one of the centers looked for a waste basket.

"You still gonna run at him like you did last night?" someone asked. "Probably," I said. But I didn't. Hung over and tentative, the Firebirds looked like they had swapped uniforms with their opponents. We weren't getting blown out, but we were losing and there's nothing more aggravating than losing to a team you had already beaten the day before after a ten hour trip.

In the third period, however, something happened that changed things for me forever. One of their wingers challenged me in the corner for a loose puck. A young kid – cocky – linemate of Bertrand. On open ice, he would probably have emerged with it, but in a corner, with my two hundred twenty pounds leaning into him, he had no chance. But as soon as I cleared it, he belted me from behind, and as we fell, he ended up on top. His face was six inches from mine and he held me down for no particular reason than to show me he could do it. So I smashed him in the face with my right hand and the butt-end of my stick just to show him he couldn't.

I felt my gloved hand collide with his nose, pushing it to the side, and I saw the taped butt end of the stick gouge him just under the left eye. Blood spurted out of the cheek wound and the nose looked broken. There is a thin line hockey players observe and I had just crossed it: I had deliberately cut a guy's face. Maybe if we weren't losing or if he had been fifteen years older or if I had been fifteen years younger, none of this would have happened, but it did.

In fact, it happened so quickly and so decisively that he didn't even bother heading back to the Rattler's box but skated off leaving a trail of blood on the arena ice all the way to the exit. I skated back to my box for a shift change. Nobody knew what happened. Because play had moved to their end, neither the refs or my teammates really saw it. They just saw the blood and the kid skating off. When my teammates looked over, I was slowly removing my pads and loosening my skates. I never skated another shift as a Firebird. The Rattlers won by five goals. When the teams shook hands at the end of the game, the red-helmeted winger skated right by me. I couldn't blame him.

. . .

Even if the hot winds hadn't come up out of the South to turn our artificial outdoor ice into slush, I knew it was over – season, career, my time in Laramie. I finally finished my degree. Then I had my surgery. That was a joke too. The doctor who was doing my physical found one of those lumps doctors find. I told him it was probably caused by an errant puck but he frowned and said he'd have to go in and take a look. When I woke up, I was minus one ball and the quack never did tell me if it was even cancer. Marginal cells, he said. After that, I had absolutely no desire to return to the Firebird locker room.

My guess is Richard Bertrand will play for the Rattlers until he loses the other eye – or worse – even after his wife takes the kids and moves back to Minnesota. You can see it coming. There are really very few surprises for an old hockey player. That's why we need our legends.

As for me, I've got a decent job at last and have settled in for the long haul. I put my son into Mite hockey but he never liked it – just as well. Every once in a while I dig out my hockey stuff and drive over to the rink to find a pick-up game. If someone asks if I used to play hockey, I'll tell them about the Firebirds. But nobody here has ever heard of them.

Dale Jacobs

The Middle of America

In the middle of America it's hard to love
the carom of the puck around end boards
stained rubber black.

It's hard to spend a Saturday night without
Hockey Night in Canada, the Leafs against
the Canadiens again from the Forum.

It's hard to remember the spray of ice
shaved by blades just edged in
the rink's tiny dressing room.

It's hard to explain what it means to ice
the puck or be off-side, to break a rule
or cross a line only you know exists.

It's hard to feel the puck on the blade
of your stick, the movement from forehand
to back, the rhythm of wood on ice.

It's hard to see a sheet of ice after the first
flood of the morning, the steam rising
like your breath as you circle the goal.

It's hard to judge the distance you've come from
hamburgers and grilled onions that seemed
the same in every arena where you ever played.

It's hard to turn to the third page of the local
Sports Section, to find hockey has the same
coverage as dog racing.

It's hard to watch how the line between player
and spectator solidifies, the ball you never
carried heavier than any stick you ever held.

In the middle of America, it's hard not to love
football, invent a past, blocking sleds and nickel
defences replacing hockey sticks and power plays,
even though you can still feel the tape's rough
back as you wrap it around the heel of a new stick.

John Grey

Mucking it Up in the Corners

The puck, the fastest thing alive,
can also slow to the grind
of unoiled machinery.
It's not always the sleek missile
stroked with elegant power
from end to end.
It's banged
between body and boards
like a punch-drunk fighter
or creeps along the curve
like a prisoner trying to break out
of its jail of sweaty bodies.
The puck doesn't just belong
to the sleek gazelles.
Sometimes, it slides into
the scrappy domain
of the lumbering buffaloes,
is thumped and slapped at
like one more chest or jaw.
No, the puck does not always
sip champagne with the chairman
in his luxury box.
Mostly, it's up in the stands
with the hollering crowd,
trapped like the tonsils
in their screaming lungs.

Dan Hammond, Jr.

For Next Year

I flop too soon.

On my side, defenseless, watching it rise slower and lower than anticipated. I can see that and my mind comprehends it, but my body continues to act on impulse, recalling the past, waiting for the expected. My right arm surges high into the air, anticipating impact. But the shot has been flipped. It moves agonizingly close under my outstretched arm. It taunts me, nicks my chest, glances off the pads. I can read the letters of the puck, CHL, as it eases its way by and into the net.

As others dart around slashing icy slivers with severe, almost savage turns, I remain stapled to the ice. Thoughts race unfettered, leaping synapse after synapse, but my body moves as if the connecting tissues have congealed. I am becoming a dualist.

The shooter, Tonelli, cuts behind the net. He laughs, not for joy, but for menace. It is his second goal of the period, their fourth. If Dickinson, our back-up goalie, had not been injured last week, I would be replaced. At thirty-four, I again contemplate retirement.

As the other side celebrates, my teammates slide towards the bench, embarrassed, or in the defensemen's case, guilt-ridden. Four goals in fifteen minutes, three on breakaways. Eleven saves. I am spent.

Using my stick, I rise and grab the water bottle from the top of the net. I am dehydrated. I empty it and throw the bottle towards the bench. Two bottles come back at once. At least they are thinking of me. I throw one back.

I ease through the crease and bend into the net. Closing my eyes, I hear the barbs spewed from the crowd, but somehow, in here, they do not disturb me as much.

"Hey, Geng, you suck!"

"Your mother could have stopped that one, Geng."

"Hey, Geng, your mother sucks, too!"

They laugh. Mom lives in a retirement home in Wisconsin. I exist in the netherworld of hockey – Fort Worth, Texas.

. . .

The ice is melting. What the hell do you expect during March in Texas? It's the first day of spring and I long to be in a tanktop, shorts and rollerblades. Instead, I move through the slush carrying forty pounds of extra baggage, wondering if this is my last game.

It didn't have to be. If we had won Friday night, today's game would have decided who made the playoffs. Now, we pack it up and head for home in a couple of hours. My flight leaves at 7:05 PM. Wisconsin-bound. Not much time to shower and get to the airport, but I am anxious to leave.

This could have been a great game, one to remember. As it is, today is meaningless. Tomorrow, even more so. We move slowly, with trepidation, playing tentatively to avoid upset and injury. The other side skates with swiftness, abandon, concerned only with the game. Their minds, not burdened with thoughts of next season or the season after that, focused on today. They must prepare only for the next game.

Shit-fire! Not only has the puck escaped our end but that son-of-a-bitch Tonelli is coming with it.

“Ride him off!” I yell to Red, but he lazily swipes at the puck and Tonelli is past him again.

I come out of the net and cut off his angle, but he dekes and I commit left as he moves the puck to my right. I reach back with my stick and somehow poke it away before he can take aim. Red moves into the net until I recover and for the first time today the fans give a half-ass cheer.

We hold our ground. The green light comes on and we move dully towards the locker room amid the boos and catcalls.

“Hey, Geng!” I hear the familiar shrill.

I know.

I suck.

. . .

A puddle of sweat gathers between my skates. It rolls from my face with a constant, steady rhythm – an I-V drip, equal parts water and vodka. I stopped drinking around four; the game started at two. Ten hours is not sufficient time to move that much vodka out of my system.

Water circulates non-stop around a malfunctioning urinal. It has been stuck for weeks, but no one fixes the damn thing. It is the only sound. Normally Coach Rossetti would be screaming his lungs out, like he did Friday night. Today, he doesn’t give a shit. Like us. His plane tickets lie on top of his desk.

Murphy and Popolov move toward the door. Others slowly follow. As is customary, my superstition, my little quirk, I am the last player out the door. A few yards from the ice stands Mother. She was in the shower when I left her apartment this morning. I hope she is not pissed. I didn’t stick my head in to say “goodbye.” Some women take offense at that.

But not Mother. Her eyes are soft and dewy as I approach. She smiles warmly and touches every player as they move past. I lag further behind just in case she has some word of endearment for me or gives some indication that she and I spent last night together. I do not want the others to know.

Mother is our business manager. A tall, not striking, but certainly noticeable redhead with a forceful, authoritative stride which belies her caring, even nurturing attitude with the players. I wouldn't call her a touchy-feely person, but she is, at least, a hands-on type.

She has been Mother so long, no one knows her actual name. Most of the kids like Langston and Pelphrey think they could nail her. But as I expected, she exists in that shady area around forty, hence, is old enough to be their mother. Not mine.

"You want that I should grab a stick and put on some pads?" she asks.

"Sure as hell couldn't hurt," I reply.

The music blares as Murphy steps onto the ice. Jagger screams, "Start Me Up" and a few die-hard fans begin to clap. Mother leans close to my ear and says, "I put 8,000 fannies in those seats and it looks like *Night of the Living Dead* out there. Can you get something going for me? Stir it up a little?

I know what she means and I have no problem with it.

"I'll buy you a defenseman," she adds enticingly. "Somebody to ride Tonelli off the puck next year or at least trip the son-of-a-bitch."

"What next year?" I ask and move on.

. . .

I half-split, dip the pads and mark my territory from left post to right. I back into the net, close my eyes and wait for the face-off.

Mother wanted more. When she saw I wasn't up for it, she backed off and held my head to her chest. I had desired this more than the sex. I was not hard enough, had not lasted long enough, and it had not been anything nearly as satisfying as being pressed to her bosom and listening to the steady, soothing sounds of her heart.

I should have remained satisfied in her arms, stayed put, at rest. Instead, I rolled a nipple into my mouth and sucked slowly. Mother moaned. I made my mouth small and moved it between my teeth. Her pelvis began grinding against me. I wanted to show her how good I could be, how the first time had been a fluke, how I could high stick with the best of them. It swelled but wouldn't harden, and I wouldn't go through that again. I collapsed against the pillow and feigned sleep.

Mother stroked my back with her lengthy nails. Occasionally, she would run her fingers through my long hair and kiss my shoulder or the back of my neck. She did this, I presume, until I slept. Maybe longer. It did not seem to concern her, this half-ass performance from a fading goaltender. It did not seem to concern her, this recent tendency of mine to flop too soon.

. . .

Tonelli is a thug. His skills have diminished and he has slowed noticeably since we were teammates with New Jersey. Yes, the National Hockey League. An expansion team, the Devils, for one season. Tonelli lasted for almost two before being injured, traded and cut by Hartford.

Since then, we have migrated south taking different paths, step-by-step down the ladder of professional hockey. We hang on, old enough to know we have no chance of returning north; young enough to hold fast to the dream.

Tonelli slides his lazy ass back near the crease and waits like a pig for some slop to be shoveled his way. He is out-of-shape, so he lurks near my net, hoping for a rebound or some cheap way to score. He is easily prodded into fights but today, even he appears distracted, somewhat passive. We call him Smelly. Smelly Tonelli.

When he is close enough, I slip my stick around his skate and pull hard. Before Tonelli hits the ice, I have pushed Red on top of him. Red may not be worth a damn on defense, but he is one hell of a fighter. I skate away. For the first time today, the cheers from the crowd are throaty, guttural and genuine. I look to Mother and she smiles, giving me a thumbs up. Yes, I have stirred it up. The fight lasts for a couple of minutes with a minimum of blood.

As the referees sort out penalty times, I slide back into the net and close my eyes. Someone slaps a stick on the crossbar and disturbs my moment of peace. It is Murphy.

"Tighten up, shithead!" That is all he says as he skates away.

Grybinski follows. "Fuck these guys. We'll ride Ôem off your ass. You don't let nothin' through."

Sometimes, all it takes to awaken people is a simple whack in the face, a little blood on the ice and a short stint in the penalty box where thought is limited to the conception of a subtle means of retribution.

. . .

This time, voices echo through the locker room drowning out the incessant noise from the urinal. We have gained, if not the lead, at least a measure of self-respect. Four-to-two.

I cannot believe it's about to end, the final period of a mediocre career. And then what? My brother's siding business? That's Mom's choice. I used to be the one they would dote on. But ever since the Devils cut me, they have, no, Mom has held Gabe in highest esteem. He pulls down six figures in what Mom terms a "stable" business. She says what I do has no consequence, no significance.

Since Dad's death, Mom has become more blunt in her manner, unforgiving in her temperament. I did not realize or did not know the role Dad played in our family. He was a buffer. He would sculpt and trim Mom's harsh judgments, transforming them into less hostile, less threatening mother-like phrases. She is harder than I could have ever imagined. Mom was never warm, never the type to part freely with a hug or embrace, but I had no idea she could be so cold, so distant. She exudes a sense of apartness. Poor Dad.

Coach Rossetti enters the room and voices die out one-by-one until there is silence. He smiles. We are relieved.

"You know," he says, "after Friday night, I lost all faith in you bastards. But what you just did out there, it kind of restored my belief in you guys. It even recharged my batteries a little. Listen, I'd like to show these motherfuckers that we should be the ones in the playoffs. If it had come down to this one game, I'd like them to know in their heart-of-hearts that we were the best. And next year –," his voice trails off but returns with new energy and force, "– next year, by God, we'll own the bastards.

"If you want to win, I mean, *really want to win,* if you're ready to go balls out for the next twenty minutes, I'll coach this last period. Anything less and you can do your own goddamn thing out there. Now, who wants to play? Who wants to play *this game* like there's no tomorrow?"

Murphy whacks his stick against a row of lockers, once, twice, three times, building a slow, grinding rhythm. Red hits his stick on the floor. Langston and Pelphrey follow suit. I stand and slam the water cooler time and again.

It is primal, wild, electric. The pounding which began in anger and frustration is transformed into a joyful, unifying experience. We are no longer sour and jaded professionals but kids preparing to take the ice for the first time. Anything seems possible as we pound the numbing lethargy from our game, replacing it with a light and innocent enthusiasm.

Popolov limps to his locker and removes something shiny from a bag. He moves into the restroom. Langston and Pelphrey follow, banging their sticks along the way. The rest of us crowd our way toward the urinals. Sticks pound the floor in unison. Click, click, click, click, echoing around the porcelain.

I cannot see Popolov but others who can smile like fiends, like little kids defying their parents. Coach Rossetti covers his ears just as the blast occurs. The rifle's report saws through my head like some revved-up power tool. A moment of stunned silence ensues. Then laughter. Relief and release.

As the others file out making their way back onto the ice, I stand next to Popolov. Water gushes from the hole in the wall. The non-stop urinal is gone.

"Funking good shoot, eh?" he asks, butchering word and tense.

"Whatever you say, Serge. But why?"

He gives me a crooked, world-weary smile. "Can't think with loud, loud, loud, all the time."

"You mean the noise. It bothers you?"

"Yes, yes," he answers. "Can't think of game. Can't get mind good for game."

I nod.

"Got tired of funking thing."

. . .

They come in waves. If I stop one, another follows in his path and another after him. They pitch tents around my net during their power play. Relentless bastards. For two minutes, I am a target, a marionette twitching from one side to the other, wanting to be hit, hit and hit again.

A slap shot ricochets off my blocker. A rebound glances off my skate. A flip shot bounces crazily along the ice and I am lucky to snare it in my glove. The fans count down the last few seconds of the penalty and as that wild man, Popolov, charges out of the penalty box, they stand and cheer. They yell for me, for the penalty killer.

As the puck moves to the other end, I glance towards Mother. She is caught up in the game, on the edge of her seat, face flushed and hopeful. I can't remember if she seduced me or vice versa.

Mother said she married once, but it didn't work. The doctor determined her husband's sperm count to be more than adequate. The problem rested with her, she said. Mother attempted a couple of high-price methods to have a baby but nothing worked. She finally said "no more." She had wanted to adopt but her husband refused. He wanted one of his own. They argued. He called her "barren." She filed for divorce.

Mother is an only child and childless. She fills her loneliness with twelve-hour days, creating a desire for bush league hockey in a city that understands only two sports – football and more football. But, hey, she has 8,000 people sitting around the ice on a day made for being outside, warmed by the sun.

I return my gaze to the other end just in time to see Pelphrey wind up and send a slap shot sizzling into the net. The fans leap out of their seats. Their roar sends chills down my limbs. I look again to Mother. She jumps up and down several times and then looks my way. Her smile is charged with adrenaline, inspiring. Mother's hands become fists and like others on the first row, she begins beating the glass. God, she must love this game.

It is no longer meaningless. The game is notable in and of itself. Coach Rossetti barks out encouragement. I pour water over my face and feel it trickle down my chest. I slide back into the net and close my eyes. But they do not stay closed. They open and search again for Mother. She leans, face flush against the glass, distorting her features.

A different song begins playing – a singular, thumping disco beat. The Village People. For some reason, the fans love this. They sing along and dance with abandon. "Y-M-C-A … Y-M-C-A …"

Mother reaches to a child across the aisle, takes both her tiny hands and sways from side-to-side. I am already half in love.

. . .

Water, water, everywhere. The wounded wall bleeds where Popolov delivered the fatal blow. We search for dry places, lifting our skates from the slimy floor.

We should be showering, blow-drying, hand-shaking and waving good-bye, but instead, we rest for overtime. I have extended my career a few minutes longer. For the moment, I am relieved.

The thought crossed my mind to let one of their shots get through, to end it in regulation, to head for Wisconsin. Nobody would have suspected a thing. I could have let one slip between my legs or just slide around my skate. A slap shot could have sailed by my glove or I could have just flopped too soon. I couldn't do it. It's not what I want. I want to play.

Coach Rossetti is full of smiles and slaps on the back. He even offers to let anybody go who has an early flight. The price of a plane ticket may be chump change in the NHL, but here, it's a chunk. Still, no one takes him up on his sudden generosity.

I have spent thirteen seasons, not only knocking down pucks but watching all the action in front of me. You never know if or when a group of players will come together, in fact, become a team. I can sense it happening here. Something special has taken place today, win or lose. I am almost sorry I won't be here next year to see where it leads.

We trudge toward the ice one final time. Mother whispers as I go by. "You're going to miss your flight."

"I know."

"You can stay with me," she says.

I plan to say, "no thanks" or "I've made other arrangements," but it comes out, "Thank you." I set one skate on the ice but before the door closes behind me, I turn to Mother and ask, "Hey, can I call you something else? I mean, a real name or something?"

She smiles and says, "Teresa."

I return to the crease. I half-split, dip the pads and mark my territory from left post to right. I back into the net, close my eyes and it hits me. Mother is laughing, I'm sure. I've been had.

. . .

Does brother Gabe have days like this in the siding business? How many people cheer when one of his sales people gets some poor chump to sign on the dotted line? Does the finance manager jump from her seat when a customer's credit history shows no foreclosures and a minimum number of late payments? How does it work out there? How can you look forward to the next day when there's no crowd, no teammates, no clear victories or losses?

Nothing can replace this game. When it's over, part of me, more than I care to realize, will wilt and shrivel. I am not aware of anything that can replenish such a loss. Mom says I am immature, that I am unwilling to grow up and become part of the real world. A world of high-resolution boredom, bleak and toneless.

Tonelli wreaks his revenge. Away from the puck, when both referees have their attention diverted, Smelly Tonelli whacks Red across the back of the legs with his stick. Red crumples to the ice. Murphy blind-sides Tonelli with an elbow to the back of the neck. All hell breaks loose. More blood is spilled during this skirmish, but nobody is damaged. Just some short-term pain. Nothing serious. Not even a stitch.

The referees have seen only the retaliation, none of the initiation. They put us into a two-man disadvantage for the final minutes of overtime. We are screwed.

Winning is no longer the issue. The contest has been reduced to survival. Like a chess match. When at a disadvantage, one player skillfully maneuvers his defense into a position where only a draw is possible. The draw becomes a victory of sorts, particularly when the two engage in a rematch. Next year.

Coach Rossetti shrugs his shoulders and holds up his fingers in the sign of a triangle. He winks at me. We have little choice. Pelphrey will be out front chasing the puck; Popolov and Langston will swing down making up the bottom of the triangle. I slide back into the net one last time and close my eyes.

"Hey, Geng," I hear the cry. "I don't care how good you play, you still suck. Suck, suck, suck."

I come out of the net and take a drink from my water bottle. I size up the distance and slide slowly towards the voice.

"You suck, man!" He bounces as he shouts. "Really suck, dude."

I hurl the half-filled bottle into the stands and it lands with a thud in the empty seat next to my heckler. I look towards Mother as she motions to a security guard. When I reenter the net, a voice cries, "I paid for this seat, man, let go. Let go, man. This sucks. This really sucks."

. . .

Tonelli skirts along the edge of my peripheral vision. He has moved about forty feet away, no longer groveling nearby like a swine, but lurking, just out of harm's way like a vulture. Blake has the puck on the other side. He and Moreau pass it between them with Pelphrey chasing back and forth. A brutal, exhausting game of keep-away.

Suddenly, Blake slides a hard pass into our soft middle. From the corner of my eye, I see Tonelli charging in. It's a great pass. Tonelli and the puck should arrive at the same time. He doesn't slow down. He bowls me over, my back crashing into the corner where goal post and crossbar meet. For a moment, it feels as if I will be impaled. But the goal breaks loose from its moorings. Tonelli and I land against the boards entangled in each other's arms and legs. His face rests against my mask. We are too tired to fight.

"Jesus, Smelly, what the fuck are you trying to do to me?"

"Is it over?" he asks.

"No, you idiot. You knocked the net out." I try to rise.

"Hey!" Tonelli shifts his weight, halting my efforts to get up. "Just lay here for awhile. You act like a goddamn rookie. Rest. Act hurt or something."

Our teammates finally pry us apart. As we are helped to our feet, I turn around before Tonelli skates away.

"Hey, Smelly. Are you coming back next year?"

"Yeah," he answers. "Like what in the fuck else am I gonna do?"

"Ever consider aluminum siding?"

His laugh comes in short, semi-automatic bursts like a machine gun. I remember this laugh. I remember how it would wash over me during practice or in the locker room. How it would lift my spirits on some crappy road trip. He skates to the bench, removes his helmet and shoots me a jack-o-lantern grin.

I skate in circles near Mother as they put the goal back into place.

"Hey, Mother Teresa."

She smiles.

"I want Tonelli, get me Tonelli," I say.

“What do you mean?” she asks, raising her palms into the air.

“You promised me a defenseman,” I answer. “For next year. I want Smelly.”

I glide through the crease but am too weary to get into my routine. I slide back into the net, relieved it won’t be the last time. My eyes close. When I dream, this is where I long to be. Surrounded by ice, I am sustained by sudden and unexpected pockets of warmth.

Christine MacKinnon

Bladed Grace

When my brother Joe Howard was 15, he tried to jump a train and slipped. Doctors were able to save his life, but not his legs. With help, support, and gritty determination, he made a full recovery, learning even, with prosthetics, to walk again. He learned quickly which of his old haunts were handicapped accessible and which were not. He learned to deal with awkward stares and pitying offers of help. And the rest of us learned, in the most profound way, that one's essence does not live in one's body.

Eventually, he had his life back – he returned to school, worked, dated – essentially, did everything he'd done before. He discovered that lesson we are taught since childhood may be trite, but it is true: it's what's inside that counts.

There was one exception, and for my brother, it was the most important thing. At the time of the accident, Joe was an all-star hockey player, and his soul couldn't skate. He'd been on the ice since he was four. It was all he'd ever wanted to do, and he was gifted. As a goalie in the local Youth Hockey League, he had a two-year period where no one scored on him. He was taking high school business classes; when asked why, his answer was always the same: "Because I'm going to be a professional hockey player, and I'll need something to fall back on."

In Joe's case, it wasn't a pipe dream, it was true. He was the rarest of 15-year-olds: he knew exactly what he wanted to do with his life and he had the talent and commitment to attain it. He could have gone to college anywhere he'd wanted, and it was fully expected he'd one day skate across the Boston Garden ice.

Until two years ago, his hockey fanaticism, though it never waned, was limited to following the Bruins and arm-chair managing Steve Kasper. Then he was asked to play on a local sled hockey team.

Strapped to a double-runner sled, he uses two miniature sticks, with metal picks fastened to the end, to charge across the ice. Magically, he is again bladed grace, this time as a forward, playing with talent and passion. He trained hard, competed fiercely, and now wears red, white, and blue on his chest and number 23 on his back. This year, he represented the United States in the Paralympic Games in Nagano. He is one of 1,165 athletes from 190 countries competing on an international level. Joe, now 31, is fulfilling the potential we thought had been lost with his legs: he is a hockey player.

After the first preliminary game, my sister told me that Joe had gotten into a tussle with four of the opposing players. "They popped him," she explained, the sled hockey version of tripping. As upright players sometimes try to slow their opponents by throwing them off balance, the para-athlete's answer to this is to pop a wheelie and come down hard in front of their rival. Often, this causes the foot bar to strike the player in the face. In my brother's case, it dislocated his shoulder.

As I listened to my sister relate this story, I was livid, until I realized I was doing exactly what Joe hated most: I was expecting him to be treated differently because he was an amputee. "It's real hockey," he and his teammates have explained endlessly, and hockey is a physical sport. The periods are five minutes shorter, but all the rules are exactly the same.

Real hockey, I remembered, and my indignant anger faded to incredulous pride. He's still that good, that his speed and precision make the competition nervous. He put on his blades and took to the ice, and he got hurt.

Just like anyone else.

John B. Lee

Last Night it Snowed

Last night it snowed
and the world is deeply packed

so I head out early
with my little shovel
and cut cubes big as beer cases
in the driveway
which grows by slow gray sections
towards the faraway curb.

All morning I lift these measured die
and tip them one by one over the chain-link fence
for I need to tunnel out the car
...hockey's at three...
and I need to tunnel out the car
...I need to tunnel out the car
blinking like a troubled mole
I look at the milky winter sun
then forge my body forward
bent and straightened bent and straightened
like a wire someone's trying to snap.

I will suffer
the imperatives of weather
no less than boys who'll work three hours
cleaning an outdoor pond
for the thrill of an afternoon of shinny
where under a cold white moon
they'll rush and chase and clip
until worried mothers call them freezing home
their nostrils glued with ice.
And so I sweat and grind my shovel mouth
through inner songs
that play my breath
till I am walking in between hospital walls
of snow and heaving at the door of my garage,
thus are such obstacles to the game
a stony madness for this tired Sisyphus
to push aside
and find another Lazarus revived within his skin.

Clare Ferguson

Hockey and Family: A Personal Reflection

Hockey for many Canadians is akin to breathing. When friends sometimes say to me "It's just a game, for heaven's sake" I wonder how we could have grown up in the same country. Just a game? They have missed the whole point. Hockey is life. There is nothing like it for bringing people from all walks of life together, rooted in one purpose - to cheer on the team. I say one purpose but on reflection that does not seem to be true. Certainly in our family each of us has a different reason for loving the game and all the hype that surrounds it.

Hockey has been a part of my life for as long as I can remember. Some of my earliest memories are of watching hockey in the 60's with my dad on our old black and white TV. I cheered for the Leafs but my dad, a fan of technique and finesse rooted for the Habs. Dave Keon and Tim Horton were household names. I remember skating outside in our backyard rink, downtown on the pond, and even on our dead end street when it got icy enough. My father grew up in England and learned to skate relatively late so he seemed to realize how important it was for us to learn young such an important part of our culture.

My son is nine and has been skating since he was 3. He is in his third year of organized hockey. Last year he played all-star; he represented the city and the whole family traveled everywhere, wearing our green, gold and black with pride. The other parents felt like family to us. Thrown together in early October we barely knew each other. A weekend tournament, and 72 hours spent together with barely a break took care of that. From that moment on we were one. Vigilantly we shouted our cheers, the boys (and one girl) on the ice pointedly ignoring us. My son once told me we were irritating so we shut up for two games. The ref was always against us and the other team was always bigger and much more aggressive. Our kids were always the best, no matter what the score. It was a whirlwind year and at the end of the season the thought of breaking for the summer was too wrenching for some of us. We played summer hockey with our friends from the team and eagerly awaited the next season's all-star tryouts.

Then the unthinkable happened. My son was cut from the team. He was replaced with another goalie who had played at a lower level the year before. He was devastated and I could hardly comfort him, the pain was too raw even for me. My pain lasted much longer than his. He adjusted quite well to his new team but I missed my friends. I missed the green and gold sweaters with the city names on them. I missed the travel, the hours, sometimes days spent at the arena. This year he averaged only 1 or 2 ice times per week. We're close to the end of the season and I still find I don't know the other parents as well as I'd like to. Last night however, in a playoff game the other team scored with only a minute to go and I felt it again, the pull together of moms and dads. Cheering on the team. "Go, go you can do it! Dig, dig, get the puck! Shoot shoot!" And then it happened with only 10 seconds left in the game. We scored and tied the game. The crowd erupted and I felt Happiness so great I thought my heart would burst. I no longer needed the fancy sweaters or the matching jackets and bags. I could feel the same kinship with a different group of parents. What had moved me was the hockey. At any level, it's all that counts.

The importance of hockey in my husband's life is something of a joke in our house. He has difficulty making it to the office by nine but a 7:00 am practice is no problem. He bounds out of bed brimming with energy, usually waking up the rest of the family. That way we all have the opportunity to experience the joy of early morning hockey whether we want to or not. To watch my husband enter an arena is to watch him become the man he planned to be. His head snaps up, his shoulders back and the weariness of life drains from him visibly. In the hockey world, he is king. He holds court outside the arena with the smokers, shivering in the cold, where they discuss the game to come and the one played before. They moan about the injustice of the refereeing, the stupidity of the coaches. How could they play that kid on defense? Everyone knows he was born to play centre. They are positive that the kids on the other team are way bigger than ours. Nobody is exempt from their scorn; they laugh and slap each other on the back and don't come in until the team is on the ice. Only then do they file in and stand in the back row to offer up words of wisdom throughout the game. " Hey ref, what is that? Can't you see there's two teams out there?" "Ah, come on - he just touched him" and finally when the other team is called offside by an inch, "Good call ref! Way to go stripes!"

I love my husband most during hockey season because he is alive and passionate. I don't mind the long days, early morning practices, snowy drives and cold toes, I am just happy to see him lose the pressures of work, if only for an hour. I love to see him care about something and in doing so he makes us all feel cared for. There is never a lull in the conversation during hockey season and there are certainly no empty days.

Hockey for my son is just plain fun. At his games he simply stops all the pucks he can and then goes home. He doesn't carry the anguish of loss or the exhilaration of winning for longer than fifteen minutes after a game. For me, hockey is bonding with my family and with other families. For my husband hockey is the language and the place where he is most comfortable. It is a world apart from reality where he can feel secure. For many Canadians hockey is a source of huge national pride. Hockey is a microcosm of life and I wouldn't live mine any other way.

Scott Boylston

Captains by Default

The snow is delicate and knee high. It is cotton candy in my mouth, too fleeting to satisfy but enjoyable just the same. I bend in mid stride and shovel the powder with my gloved hand. With this motion I leave a smooth and straight gully that strikes me as the most perfect consequence of my effort, conspicuous in its complete lack of fault. I pack the snow against the roof of my mouth and suck it of its moisture. The remains trickle down my throat.

We trudge over the white curves of the golf course in tempered anticipation, led by Brad. His shin pads thrust forward and spoil the chaste evenness of the snow as clots of it roll across the surface with each footstep. Brad is like his father, neither tall nor short. His broad shoulders buttress a head of dirty blond hair and keen eyes. The eyes are steadily indifferent, the hair as straight as his stance. When we play dibble in the lake, the stick is most often found in Brad's grasp.

Behind him. Tim concentrates with narrow diligence on the impressions left by Brad. He is smaller than Brad in every way. He walks with his head down and his eyes rapt on the heels in front of him. His is the pursuit of a disciple, convinced of salvation through emulation. He follows Brad this way through grass and mud as well as snow.

The pond is a smudge in the distance. It borders a brief but dense wood that stands like an oasis upon the sculpted rolls of the course. It is a rectangular basin with steep, powder-packed banks that serve us well as backboards. On the far corner is a pump that runs year-round, in a small wooden shed, isolated on its perch. On one side it is braced by a thicket of evergreen and on the other side by the tar-black water it refuses to let freeze. Its influence reaches ten feet in each direction, the resulting hole the only blemish on the otherwise smooth ice. There is no desire within our group to explore the monotonous groans and darkened windows of the pump house or the lightless hole it creates in the ice. It is never mentioned between us.

I am third in line. I follow without the thought of being led. The terrain of the golf course is as familiar to me as the musty crawl space that extends from the cellar of my house. I recognize slouching firs that have sheltered trenched and tunneled forts stocked with snowball grenades and icicle rations, sand traps that have served as bunkers in warmer weather, and broad oaks and maples that still hold skeletal remains of meticulously built tree forts attended to more during their construction than any time after. This familiarity has not tarnished my intrigue, but has allowed it to prosper.

Stan and Ian Finch walk in unison behind me. They are often mistaken for twins. The actual discrepancy in years is secreted by their equal eagerness to please, just as a retriever and her grown pup can appear to be from the same litter. They are not bothered by this, not even Stan, the elder of the two, but relish the low profile and anonymity of sharing an identity. Halloween finds them draped in matching white sheets. They have eye holes and slits for their mouths that are smeared with chocolate and spit. They have been ghosts for several years and have no complaints.

Each winter we vow to recover the countless pucks that slap into the inky water like skipping stones before finally nose diving, or skid to the brink at a taunting crawl only to slip over the edge just at the moment we thought they would stop. We joke that soon an island of black rubber will rise from the murky water like a volcano, and we will make a fortune selling the black discs by the truckload. But by spring's resurgence we have other crusades in mind.

We each bring two pucks – the oldest ones we can find – pocked with misuse on summer-heated asphalt. If luck accompanies us out, and we do not lose all of our pucks, we play until the scarcity of light assigns all objects the same color, then we reluctantly retrace our path in the moonglow. We are careful not to pass too close to the wooded areas where shadows from the creaking branches hang like webs on the blue surface of the snow. We still harbor the fears of childhood, after all. The journey back may take minutes or hours, interrupted by tussles or snow angel exhibitions or lying on our backs watching our own huffs of breath against the velvet sky. We are each the last soul on earth then. We move only with regret, urged by a tingling of our backsides and the inevitable tickling itch growing around our feet that will stay with us long after the warmth of home has chased away the cold from our bodies.

Virgil trails the pack by several yards. If not for his sheer inability to brave the untrod snow without quickly losing pace, he would set his own course. He is stronger in mind than in body. His insistence that the pond can be reached more quickly by first walking farther north on the road rather than trekking directly across the contours of the blanketed course falls on deaf ears. We cross this way because the rest of us agree with Brad when he says it is more fun to create your own trail. Virgil's disinclination is worn on his face and posture. He drags his equipment behind him, like a dog on a leash, through the snow. Virgil's opinions, no matter how vehemently conveyed, encourage scorn from Brad and wary disregard from the rest of us. He is mouse-like with a red nose that runs with things better left unseen. His hair is matted as if he has just taken off a baseball cap for the first time in weeks. His appearance is irksome. His demeanor, in response to our continuous dismissal, has grown to match his appearance.

Virgil refuses to shoulder his equipment-clad hockey stick, and his skates occasionally clank in protest. He breathes heavily, martyred. We weave through the concealed hazards of the golf course behind Brad like a row of railway cars. We cross the open spaces as soldiers on the march, fully armed, our weapons slung cocksure over our shoulders. Our feet squeak in near unison on the snow. We are Washington's men at Valley Forge, Napoleon's troops before Waterloo, Snow White's six dwarves with Grumpy at the rear rubbing his runny nose and dragging his shovel all the way. The brittle cold brings sharp sensation into our lungs and pinches our nostrils. Stillness whistles past, and we breathe like dragons.

When we reach the pond we sit on our jackets and lace up. The jackets remain as rest stops and penalty seats. We dress in our heroes' jerseys and rarely match our teammates. Stan and Ian are the exception. There are no goalies, no defenseman, no left wings, right wings or centers; there are only hockey players. We shoot for the space between our opponents' discarded boots. Over the bank is over the crossbar. To compensate for the dark pool of unfrozen water, we swing our boots toward the opposite corner.

We rarely lose a puck to the snow that surrounds the pond, and we never moan when one breaches the shallow crest. Instead there is a hysterical rush to the hidden puck and whoever recovers it is rewarded with a goal. We charge the bank, glide for a step and then, with eyes wide, we leap, knees or head first, diving into the snow and digging like mad. There are days when a thin and fragile layer of ice coats the snow and the puck leaves a telltale hole where it lands. These frenzied quests provide us with a tension breaker from our game, which we play with the violence if not the skill or talent of our idols. Tempers flare, and with them gloves and sticks fly.

I am captain by default. Tim will not willingly oppose Brad who, again by default, albeit one of a different kind, is captain of the other side. Stan and Ian refuse to step forward. Virgil is pushed back whenever he tries. I am fortified by the Finch brothers, invariably a package deal. Virgil is teamed with Brad and Tim. We play the best of five games and win because Virgil is ignored by his teammates.

We do not have periods but break on mutual exhaustion. Snow provides nourishment. We take it in slowly, wary of the dull ache that too much cold at one time will invite. We wipe past the top layers and dig into the virgin snow and bring the precious mound to our faces slowly so that none of the powder is lost. We lap at it with the hope that just once we will get more than we already know we will get. It feels good to lie still and we lob snow at each other in lazy arcs, laughing and coughing up the cold air.

Our game starts up again slowly with the more eager rising to skate in shiftless circles with a puck or ice chunk bouncing between the wooden blades of their sticks. We shuffle teammates so that I have Virgil and Tim, and the Finch brothers are with Brad. It is ancient law that Brad and I never side on the same team. It goes unsaid and unquestioned.

With the new alignment Tim passes indiscriminately, as if Virgil has just stepped onto the ice. There is no sign of the scorn so venomously exhibited in the first games. Without Brad's influence, Virgil becomes a competent teammate in

Tim's eyes. In fact, Virgil and Tim share a certain tenacity, as well as an unspoken appreciation of each other's manic drive to prove themselves. They are more like each other than either knows, or would admit. We lose ourselves in the game, breathing heavily and finding that our lungs expand in compensation. There is a freshness at the bottom of them.

Tim passes the puck in my direction, but Brad, sensing Tim's intentions, cuts between the two of us and skates at full speed toward our goal. Only Virgil is between Brad and the net, and he skates backward watching Brad's eyes. He is awkward but firm in his motion. Brad is capable of quickly getting the puck past Virgil, his wrist shot is hard and sure, but instead he thrusts forward and engages Virgil. There is a collision, but not of the sort we expect. Virgil is not flattened. Instead, the blade of his stick deftly slaps the puck away and then inadvertently slips between the stanchions of Brad's skates. Brad falls immediately onto his stomach and slides toward the snowbank. The brunt of the impact is absorbed by his head. There is a faint crunch and then silence as the rest of us skate to a halt.

The brief hush is shattered by mirth at the sight of Brad as he turns his head, nostrils packed with snow. The force of the blow has driven both his eyelids upward, and he wears a dazed smile. He blows a snow pellet from his nostril and we laugh again, but Brad is unaccustomed to this side of mockery. There is another short silence as he unsteadily rises to his skates and shakes his head free of snow, nearly losing his balance. This is too much for us. Tim slips and falls to the ice he is laughing so hard. Stan and Ian fall into a snowbank. Virgil smiles meekly and allows his body to sag in amusement.

We all look away from Brad momentarily, so no one sees him rush headlong toward Virgil. Before anyone knows what is happening he buries his shoulder into Virgil's chest. We watch him fall to the ice and curl up in pain, the breath knocked out of him. Brad skates back to where his stick has fallen and swoops to pick it up without stopping. There is no sound other than the methodical ripping of Brad's blades on the ice as he skates back toward Virgil. He wears a dubious grin we have all seen, not knowing if it reflects leniency or retribution. He glides to Virgil, who is still trying to get his breath, and hooks the blade of his stick between one of his skates. he circles him slowly so that Virgil spins on his back like a top. The apparently benign retort settles the rest of us and we chuckle at the sight. Virgil relaxes somewhat and plays along.

After several turns Brad straightens his line and tows Virgil around the pond. He turns and then turns again so that the two of them make a figure eight. We applaud the performance. The relief and appreciation of being a part of something shows on Virgil's face. He has almost forgotten the pain in his chest. They are a figure skating team. Brad goes into a tight spin and Virgil revolves around him like a satellite. There are cheers from the rest of us. Brad again breaks out of the formation and then skates to the corner furthest from the pump house and its dark moat. He pauses in the corner as if preparing to make his final pass. Brad takes a bow, careful to keep his stick high enough to prevent Virgil from freeing his foot. Uncertainty fills my stomach like syrup. Brad throws a complicit glance toward Tim, whose face quickly drains of amusement. He rises and skates toward the two and smiles with a plea. No words pass between anyone, as if we all know our roles. Brad nods toward Virgil's other skate. Tim obeys his unspoken command and hooks Virgil's free skate with his own stick. We titter as if to assure Brad that he need not take the threat any further, he is in control once again. He tips his head toward the quivering water and looks into Tim's eyes. They fuzz like cataracts.

They are forty feet away from the unfrozen area and picking up speed. Brad and Tim are on either side of Virgil, who is spread-eagle between them like the contents of a slingshot. The last hint of uneasy laughter is swallowed by the sound of steel edges cutting ice. Stan and Ian look at each other and then down to their feet. I stand when they are twenty feet away. I hope the motion alone will distract them and bring them back. Of course, it does not. Tim has abandoned his glances toward Brad and is staring ahead now in vacant obedience.

I skate into their path and yell Brad's name, but I am not there for him. The frigid pool is behind me; I am at its edge. I hear the hum of the pump, and the patient lapping of the water. I take two strides and jump at Brad. My shoulder hits him in the stomach and he leaves his feet as I push him down to the ice with a resounding crack. I think to myself that it is a good hit. I land on top of him. In one motion he rolls on top of me, punches me in the face and stands, but he is hurt. He holds his gut and bends over in pain. He skates away, laughing under his breath.

Tim, still holding Virgil by the skate, comes to a stop two feet away from the edge of the ice. There is guilt about him, then quick anger, like I spoiled his fun. He skates by and mutters an obscenity as I lie on the ice with blood dripping from my nose. He follows Brad to their boots and begins unlacing his skates. Brad already has his skates off and is bending over in pain. He continues laughing as both of them walk off the ice and into the barren landscape. They follow the same course that led them here. Brad walks in our footprints and Tim pushes through untread snow directly beside him. I look back at Virgil, but he watches each one of us without expression. We are accomplices, witnesses, one no better than the other. Our silence is our guilt. Ian's eyes have not left the ground, Stan's have not left the darkening sky. I focus my attention on the stiff blood on my skin and how the caked substance cracks when I wiggle my upper lip. The air is new within my nostrils.

The Finch brothers rise and skate slowly to their boots. Not a word is spoken as they dress for their journey home. They do not look in our direction but instead throw glances at the receding figures of Brad and Tim. Then they are up and off with a feeble acknowledgment. They walk at a slow and deliberate pace to the path and then speed up in random spurts. They run for several strides and then slow back down, almost in unison. As they move further from the pond the sprints come more frequently until they are almost galloping through the snow, plowing ahead like dogs after their master.

I come very close to laughing at the sight of Virgil. His nose is as red as I've ever seen it. He follows the progression of the Finch brothers with narrow eyes, and then lifts himself and skates past me. I think he does not realize I am there as his skate blade comes within inches of my bare hand. I know I will not move until he leaves or says something. I have no desire to speak a word to him, and I dread to hear his voice. I watch the dark ripples make their way across the flat water and bump harmlessly into the stark whiteness of ice. The pump is like a heartbeat; it drones despite the cold, despite everything. I feel as if the island of black rubber is about to emerge, as dark and still and cold as the water that conceals it. I pay no attention as Virgil makes his way across the golf course. He does not follow the others, but cuts directly across toward the road somewhere off through the trees. His progress is slow, and laborious, and irrefutable. He becomes a dot in the distance like the rest of them.

I stand and skate toward the snow bank that holds my belongings. I sit, remove my skates and rub the sleepy tingle from my feet. It is a wonderful feeling. The sun is nearly absent. It seeps through dark trees on the horizon. I walk home over untrod snow, and go out of my way to avoid our old trails. As the last glow of sun thins to purple I fall into the snow and lie still and listen to the empty creaking of winter.

Gus Pelletier

In the Heat of Gratitude

In deep winter Father
was often there,
distant as always
behind the chain-link fence
circling Carlson's Ice Rink,
watching shot after shot,
the Christmas puck-gift
coming to rest in goal.

After every score
the boy took a sweeping
rink-wide sprint,
lifted his taped-up stick
toward the faraway skies,
and the fence,
then pumped it up and down
in triumph, exhilarating joy.

Time, space intersected then,
as now: the boy-man scrawling,
resurrecting Father again,
bringing him back with thanks
for ever-so-bashful love
greater by far than how or why.
The Rink sold, the ice gone,
the fence no longer remains.

Dorothea Belanger

I Don't Get Hockey

I don't mean the language of breakaway, icing, and slashing but rather the purpose my eleven-year old son has in wearing an armour of complicated pads, shells and cups to skate full throttle after a hard black rubber disk. He gets the puck for a second or two, attracting a confusing tussle of torsos, sticks and skates, and then whoever has the strength – or is it the luck – plucks it away and the scramble continues.

It never occurred to me that one of our children would want to play hockey. I grew up with three brothers who didn't. In fact I sense my skiing family took a dim view of hockey as a coarse sport, though I don't recall whether this was ever articulated. Nevertheless, I'm eager to support our son's choice of any sport he loves for the healthy variety it will provide in his regime of school and music lessons. And I've had many of my negative preconceptions challenged. I always thought that hockey was brutish and aggressive; winning would count more than sportsmanship and team work. It is forceful but not as much as wrestling with his Dad. The slamming and speed do appear dangerous, and there are a few tears at every game, but the only body contact is hands patting helmets, consoling arms around shoulders and fists tapping when trading off the bench. The coaches make sure that everyone plays and that each player knows he is important to the team. Good pass work gets as much attention as goals. One notion holds true though. No matter how many adults tell the boys it's more important to play well and have fun, they focus only on winning. It must be primordial, this ferocious urge to win.

They started in September, and now tribalism has tightened around this team of coaches (three fathers) and players (eleven sons) when they meet for weekly games and practices. Their sponsor is Brown's Funeral Home abbreviated to Brown's Fun. Home on their jerseys, but the team name is Brown's Kanucks on the schedule. A bright pre-game buoyancy among these males overrides the sour vinyl smell in the drab dressing room of our local recreation centre. We mothers, fathers and grandparents in the stands have loosely formed a peripheral branch of this tribe, the biggest fans of Brown's Kanucks. Rink rats, siblings of the players, whirl about the one hour game, exploring the concession and bleachers, then run the deck area pausing to watch bits of the game. The chemistry among the Kanucks' families, which began casually last fall, has become warm and intensifies at a good game or tournament.

We stand at a rail or sit in hard fold-out seats and cheer our boys as the puck slips between the two nets. We shriek "C'mon guys!" There are long collective "ohs" ascending, (I squeal), when the Kanucks steer the puck in towards a goal. There are unified descending groans if we miss or the other team gets one. I never imagined myself absorbed in a clutch of hockey fans. My feet pound the concrete, I suck in air, my back is rigid, all my senses are cued to track commotion on ice around a puck. "Hustle, hustle, hustle. C'mon guys. Stick with 'em, stick with 'em." Parents cheer. Parents encourage. We did the same thing with gentler voices ten years ago when the boys were learning to walk, six years ago when they were learning to ride a bike, to swim and read. We watch and encourage. It's innate, parents' continual vigilance and it feels fitting within the arrangement of a hockey team.

In December we beat the Keewatin Senators. Nobody beats the Senators. Our team played in high-octane mode – it sparked tears. Before I understood it, I'd become emotionally involved in a sporting event, a hockey fan even! For the rest of the day everything else seemed trivial. (P.K. Page talking about her poetry on CBC radio as we drove home, normally of great interest to me, sounded frivolous.) I became more and more eager to be the one to take our son to the games, hoping to feel that drama on ice again.

Every year there are the boys who score most of the goals and a small, weak player who we all agree improves remarkably with every game. There are the pleasant, amiable boys, a saucy one who gets caught swearing, and the pitchers of the dressing room who throw balls of tape or ice off their blades. We car pool, tie their skates (still at eleven years of age!), lend equipment and root for all the boys. We're committed to one another, we've become a troupe, a team.

I've come to recognize the players by the way they maneuver on the ice. Number six is the only one who tucks his jersey in. He is a beautiful skater swinging in and out between the players – a Fred Astaire on ice. (Of course, I know never to mention this.) Numbers fourteen and sixteen are our stars. They do that break-away thing, shaking off the opposition like an irritating snag – and score! Our goalie has no idea how we adore him. He is puck-repellent. A barrier with supersonic moves, he catches the puck in his glove, lies down to block the net and is on his feet again, ready for the next onslaught. Each boy is distinctive and is known to us in the Brown's Funeral Home seats: socks over the skates, fluorescent green laces, head cocked to the side, a red helmet, an upright stance, a flying forward gait.

After a goal the scorer performs a dance. There's a little shuffle of the feet and then the arms, one at a time, punch out, out, in, in and are released in ecstasy above the head. He glides by the bench, a glove out to receive his teammates outstretched hands or they hug each other. I don't get as many hugs anymore! It's safe to hug comrades on a rink though.

The coaches set the tone for the hockey season and this year we're fortunate. We have a strategist who claps his arm around each boy as he comes off the ice and points out tactics on the ice, explaining, teaching. Another pats the head of each with warmth as they come off. Plenty of goodwill, firmly in place. The other watches the game, yells the odd tip – "pass it up the boards" – and always voices the positive – "good job, nice work" or "good pass" – every time a player swings into the doors.

. . .

Coaches and players are riveted to the battle on ice. In their purposeful faces, I see the boys the coaches were, in the boys I catch a glimpse of the men they will become – a moving sight. I'm grateful to these men, positive guides though several months of boyhood. Their presence will soak into the boys' bones for life.

I watch hard and pay attention but after five years I still feel like an alien at a hockey game. I get caught up watching the reactions of the players and coaches while that little black disc glissades to and fro on the ice. I miss much of the game. I look into the face guards when an opposing player has glued himself onto one of our guys yet the boys don't even look at each other. I guess they expect it. Or a little push and shove occurs; I can't tell when it goes from being a check to a penalty. The referee blows the whistle, the boys know instantly where to stand. Amazing. I'm not always sure why the whistle goes, what happened. The skating, passing, change of directions, it's all so fleeting.

I haven't learned the new language and customs my son has

picked up during his five years in hockey. It's like visiting him in a foreign country. At the pre-game huddle there is a rhythm. The boys pounding the ice with their sticks is followed by a whoop full of great expectations. (Where did this rhythm originate, what is its particular history?) What words float between them, inside the dome they collectively form in front of their goalie? I don't know that I want to know, probably something about kicks and the opposing teams' butts.

Watching the boys' skills improve over the years, I've been pulled into the theatrics of hockey, the excitement. I am grateful that our son has removed me from my sphere, marvel that he has brought me into his realm. Oddly, I find it a comfort to see him belong to something I didn't foresee, something he has chosen. Is this an embryonic glimmer of a man leading an independent life?

Ronn Hartviksen

Of Ice & Men

His last goal – a brilliant fake and artistic shot – ripped the puck through the tattered webbing and landed black as a pellet of coal on the white ice at the base of the end boards.

My son Galen, 15, and I had been playing one-on-one shinny on our backyard rink for over two hours. The late sun occasionally blinked at us as it dipped behind the balsam tree line on our west ridge. The temperature, -4 C, made for perfect glacial ice.

Our rules are few. No clutching, grabbing or use of the sticks as gaff. Keep the shots low on a defender, and alternate goals to attack every 10 minutes or so, just to make the angles fair for both of us. The first one to score 10 goals wins the match. Galen had just taken our best of five series, three games to two.

We've built this homemade open-air ice rink each hockey season over the past eleven years. The rink, which we call the Bean Pot, has grown from a shrimp-size original to a 30 by 20 meter structure, an evolution that has matched the growth of my son.

As he gathers up the loose puck and stick handles to center, Galen beckons. "Wanna play a quick game to three, Dad? Supper's a while yet."

"Sure," I reply, pausing to look up from the ice. "Can you see the quarter moon coming out in the night sky?" I'm trying to gain some extra breathing time before we face off.

Tonight my energy is drained, and he sees it. He glides to a corner of the rink where he has set two Cokes in a mound of snow. He uncaps his and holds the other out to me. I trail him to the bench the way he used to tack after me as a toddler. We sit silently, taking long gulps, staring across the ice. His shoulders are now almost even with mine: the kind of benchmark fathers seem to meet in the most unrehearsed and casual of places.

"After supper you've got a board meeting, eh?" he quizzes.

"Last one for a while," I chime back.

"You'll make it through the work, Dad. The 90's are only the 60's turned upside down, as you've said before. I'll plow the rink and save you some time, if you could flood later so it's ready for tomorrow?" He's bartering now.

I nod yes as we re-lace our skates. How well I remember the times I tied on his first pair of blades as his size 10 skates now move effortlessly drawing him to center.

We drop the puck once more, and Galen puts me away with three quick goals. I barely managed a few wild shots: two of them spanking off his goalposts – my timing and accuracy obviously fading into the night.

At just that moment, my wife, Margaret, flicks the rink lights, our signal for supper. As we pick up our gear, I think how precious this exhaustion will be in future years. Especially when Galen's grown again, and we two take time to witness a new moon under the dome of another winter. No matter where the Ice Age finds us.

Ken O'Keefe

Out behind Bernie's barn

a February rink
sparkling like a silver dollar
spawned in congealing flood
in an early thaw

out behind Bernie's barn
overnight a frozen flat
ensnaring village
in back acres   the Gardens

kids of sundry shapes
weighted down
hike across crusted fields
a rendezvous with hockey

dreamers
burners turned on full
stickhandle
through frenzied figures

supper hour
skate weary pros head home
a generous table
game resumes   in satisfaction

Hugh Hennedy

Windy Day Game

Lacing up the skates
You had to blow on your fingertips
The way you did as a kid
To keep some feeling in them.
It was maybe in the twenties
The day after Christmas and
The wind was blowing strong
And after a while the gang
Playing pretty good hockey
Had had enough and pushed
Their nets to shore and heaved them
Into the backs of pickups
So we who stayed or came
Late had to start over
With rocks for goals and a tossing
Out of stick for sides
And some wore no pads
And it was hard to see
The puck on the black of ice
And sliding in the slanted
Rays reflecting off it
And it took some time
Before you had a sense of

Which greens and blacks and which
Red jackets were on your side
And the ones to try to pass to
And that wind that had been
Strong enough to move a
Hockey net was still
Blowing and one of the grays
I knew now on my side
Shouted as we hung back on
Defense, Isn't this great!
And I said yes, even though
I still hadn't worked up a sweat,
Not so that you'd notice.

Tina Lincer First

In the Penalty Box: Confessions of a Reluctant Hockey Mom

It is 7 a.m. on a Sunday morning and I am visiting Pittsfield, Mass., former home of author Herman Melville. But I am a long way from the literary shrine of Arrowhead, Melville's family farmhouse and the place where he completed *Moby Dick.*

Wearing clunky boots and my warmest winter jacket, I sit in an ice rink in a century-old boys' club, wedged between hollering hockey mothers admonishing their Wayne Gretzky-worshipping sons to "Keep your stick down!" Fathers, hands in pockets, pace the wooden bleachers barking "Ice it!" or "Slap it around!" In particularly heated moments, I have been caught rising from the bleachers myself, shouting out my son's name and urging him to "Take it away!" as he tries to steal the puck from a player twice his size.

I marvel. As a writer and sometimes painter, I love to spend my time among books and art and other cultural trappings. But here I am living a double life as a parent of the starting center on the Capital Youth Hockey Mite A Travel Team, the most competitive team for the league's youngest players, ages 7 to 9. It is a job that requires more fortitude than most.

"Center it!" I yell in abandon. "Get on him!" And my favorite – "Aggravate 'em!"

No, I don't wear one of those hockey mom sweatshirts that warns, "Don't mess with me – I've been up since 4 a.m.," but I have slowly, tentatively, reluctantly skidded to the rim of that circle of intense sports parents. Not to be confused with soccer or Little League moms, hockey moms are passionate, driven, speed-worshipping slaves to ice time and the art and aura of puck control.

. . .

There's a lot I've learned in the year of the hockey travel team. I've learned to help my 7-year-old son Lucas suit up, down to the last snap of the helmet and tightening of the laces in 15 minutes flat, without swearing, pursing, panting, grumbling, whining or stalking out of the locker room in frustration at the amount of time required to get in gear.

I've become adept at heaving the 20-pound hockey bag over one shoulder while passing through narrow doorways with the agility of a Cajun dancer executing a two-step.

I've gotten accustomed to early bedtimes before games for which we must rise at 5 a.m. to be on the road by 6, in the locker room by 7:30 and on the ice by 8.

I've gotten good at fitting the demands of my job, housework, errands and my children's music lessons, homework and religious school around the practices and weekend games (as many as five during some big tournaments).

I've learned to shrug off the sidelong glances from Hebrew school teachers who clearly don't approve of, or understand, why my son misses school nearly every Sunday. I've begun, only half jokingly, to tell friends whom we barely see between the fall and spring equinoxes that we've converted from Judaism to hockeyism.

I've also become a *roadmeister extraordinaire.* I now know the fastest route from our Albany, New York home to the major ice centers in Rutland and Middlebury, Vt.; Pittsfield, North Adams, Springfield and Holyoke, Mass.; and Plattsburgh,

Glens Falls, Saratoga, Troy, Utica, Rome, Binghamton, Poughkeepsie and Millbrook, N.Y. I also can tell you how to get to the beautiful new Dollard des Ormeaux Civic Center outside of Montreal, where we traveled at the end of last season for the largest novice hockey tournament in the world to play the mighty Canadians. For the record, I even have a rinkside photo of me and "Vas-y," the tournament's French mascot.

. . .

Once upon a time, I associated a puck with Shakespeare's mischievous "Midsummer" sprite and thought of a goal as something I wanted to achieve. I didn't think about other contexts for these words until I married a man with a passion for hockey.

In the early years of my marriage, I endured many hockey games in the Adirondacks and on Long Island. But when my mate tried to explain the rudiments of the game, I tuned out. Surrounded by fans who thrilled to a good fight among players, I longed instead for a night with a good work of fiction, far from the madding crowds of rink rats.

I remember, in particular, a Saturday night in Glens Falls watching a tie game between the Adirondack Red Wings and a team whose name I've since forgotten or never knew. While fans around me yelled in apoplectic ecstasy, I yawned and looked at my watch. Already it was almost midnight, and I was anxious to get our two-year-old daughter home to bed. Holding my sleepy child in my arms, I turned to my husband, who, like the thousands of other spectators in the North Country arena that night was ensnared in the frenzy of sudden death, and said, "I've decided there's nothing I like about this sport."

That was 10 years ago. I don't remember how my spouse responded to my hockey-hating confession, but five years later, we were divorced. Neither of us listed incompatibility on the sports front as grounds for dissolution of the marriage. But these days, I look back in ironic appreciation because however our paths diverged in the ensuing years, we've met up again at the rink, where we do most of our communicating.

Lucas began skating lessons when he was 3. At 4 and 5 he was in a learn-to-play hockey program, and at 6, he joined the league's house team. In between, there were night clinics and summer camps. While his dad did his fair share of chauffeuring to these activities, it always seemed as if that's all I did – get ready for hockey, sit through hockey, unwind from hockey and air out, wash and pack the hockey garb.

Summer camp was memorable for its 90-degree days in which Lucas pulled on long underwear, protective cup, thick pants, stockings, shin guards, heavy gloves, jersey and all the other paraphernalia and we drove off together on my way to work. The car's air conditioner could never get cool enough fast enough for Lucas, who liked the camp but hated the seasonal disconnect.

The season of the House Mites, we arose at 5:30 a.m. every weekend for 6:30 a.m. practices and games. A night person by nature, I dreaded these sunrise excursions, especially when I was simultaneously trying to forge a new life as a single mother.

There were times when Lucas was at his dad's for the weekend but I promised I'd show up for a morning game. The night before, I'd be out folk or swing dancing, my newest passions, arrive home late and slump into bed with my stockings and dance skirt still on. A few hours later, I'd tumble out of bed and pull jeans and an oversize sweater on top of my dancewear before heading to the rink. With my scratchy eyeballs, yesterday's clothes and my hair yanked into a ponytail, I felt unlike all the other hockey moms I'd met.

In fact, from the start I felt as though I'd crossed the border into a foreign country. The language is different; the customs are different. There are cultural do's and don'ts. Most moms don't miss games, a fact of which they are proud. Last year, the goalie's mother held the record for missing only one practice when she was bedridden with the flu. In a six-month travel season with two practices a week and nearly 80 games, I'd call that quite a logistical feat.

Or insanity.

Get a life, I've often thought. Why don't these people get a life?

. . .

We joined the A-level travel team against my wishes. For one entire summer, Lucas' dad and I argued over this. Sitting at a picnic one afternoon in August with parents of house team members who talked eagerly about tryouts and the coming season, I expressed my reservations.

"I don't want to give up my life for hockey," I said.

The other parents looked at me as if I'd gone off the deep end.

In the end, unable to reach a compromise with my ex (I suggested a less competitive league or going with the B team, whose travel radius was smaller), I decided I'd rather drive to Buffalo in a blizzard than continue arguing. In early September, Lucas tried out and made the team; by the end of the month, practice began.

Life on the Mite A Travel Team was organized, professional and disciplined.

Coaches and parents treated the boys as though they were a mini-sized NHL franchise. Between games, designated mothers washed the jerseys; they brought them back on hangers, making sure they were the right colors (visitors or home team) for the right games. Squirt-bottle drinks were always available; no longer did I have to worry about my son's fluid intake. Before and after games, parents were made to wait outside the locker room while the coaches prepped, huddled and reviewed. There was an unmistakable sense of importance in the air. These 15 boys were the chosen. They had a mission. The rest of us – parents, siblings, grandparents – made sure nothing got in the way.

We quickly fell into a routine. My 11-year-old daughter became adept at doing her homework in the bleachers during evening practices. While other parents chatted and sized up the team, I read a book or magazine. My ex and I traded school bags and other necessities in the locker room or parking lot of the arena during our weeknight custody transfer.

The first few months on the road, I endured driving rainstorms and caravans that I struggled to keep up with. With the hockey bag stuffed in the rear of my small station wagon, obstructing my view, I drove as fast as I could to keep pace with the line of fast-moving mini-vans, utility vehicles and trucks.

Sitting in the lobby of a motel in Springfield during our first tournament weekend in October, I read my book and lamented that I didn't have one good friend I could share any of this with. Did I say share? The next day, my ex and I ended up eating a less-than-relaxing breakfast together at a cafeteria in Holyoke, one more strange manifestation of the power of hockey over all of us.

I attended more and more games, mostly on my weekends with my children, but many times even when they were with their dad. I told myself I was doing it for Lucas – being supportive, not letting our divorced status get in the way of cheering him on – but I also could feel myself becoming mesmerized by the sport.

By midwinter, I still couldn't tell you what offside meant. But as the team gelled, the level of playing was higher, the competition fiercer. Watching my son – in his #1 jersey, the littlest one and one of the youngest – throw his body and spirit into the game, I swelled with joy.

I began to appreciate that hockey was like dancing, with its own set of steps and choreography. It even had its own music, the crack of pucks slamming against the boards, the schwish of metal blades on ice. There was also the din of the crowd, the ring of cowbells and miked-in "jock n' roll" telling us to "get ready to rumble." It was its own performance art, too. In addition to the drama playing out on the ice while the glowing scoreboard numbers blinked down the time, rinkside dramas encompassed the obligatory selling of raffle tickets, the siblings' nonstop runs for candy and Slushies and the incessant team cheer, "Let's go, Capital!"

Relaxing into hockey's rhythms, I forgot about driving in bad weather, schlepping around town to sharpen blades, struggling with skate laces that were never tight enough and always running out of hockey tape. I didn't think about the smell of the locker room at 7 in the evening when I wanted out, and home, fast.

I learned to speak hockey – I could banter reasonably well about blue lines, hat tricks, power plays, penalties and wings, and eventually, I could even fake my way through offsides. I never did make it to the bookstore, as planned, to pick up "Hockey for Dummies." I didn't have time.

And then, in the middle of my evolution as hockey mom, amid the tumult and the non-stop chauffeuring, I met a man I adored, who loved art and books and dancing and a dozen other things I loved. It was as if fate were smiling at me because he also happened to be Russian, with a built-in cultural predisposition toward hockey. Suddenly I had a companion. Slowly, I brought him into the game. Life filled out.

I fantasized about getting a large cowbell.

. . .

That winter, I drove to Western New York in a snowstorm and to Vermont during a devastating ice storm. In run-of-the-mill motels I supervised games of knee hockey in which rolled up socks or hockey tape became makeshift pucks. At home, I played knee hockey with Lucas whenever we had a spare minute. We began to have some of the team members over for play dates on those rare occasions when we had a free afternoon.

At the rink, my daughter became friendly with another girl her age, and the two of them entertained the younger siblings who ran up and down the bleachers during practice and games, rivaling their hockey-playing brothers for energy and noise levels.

I could never seem to get "Let's go, Capital!" out of my head. It became my official interior soundtrack as I spun through my days. But when I ingested so much hockey I felt like I might OD, I began to bring my writing to practice. "Center it!" now became a mantra for myself. Hockey may be all-pervasive, but I'd try to carve out an island of calm in the middle of it, to stay grounded in what mattered to me.

Lucas was appalled that I was the only mother who wrote during hockey practice. How he managed to notice me scribbling away in the bleachers while he was doing his peripatetic puck chase, I don't know. But I do know he'll probably never let me forget it.

. . .

Our Mite A Travel Team season ended with a flourish in Canada. Mothers sewed American flag patches on the jerseys and bought plastic flags to wave; our team manager handed out maps and hotel details. All but one of the families took their children out of school for a day to accommodate the three-day tournament schedule.

The Dollard des Ormeaux Civic Center, a massive modern facility with three *patinoires,* or rinks, was a swirl of activity. It was the 20th anniversary of the tournament, and the center overflowed with balloons, face painters, music and vendors hawking everything from pucks and pins to hockey stick-shaped toothbrushes. Our Albany Capitals joined a roster of teams with such names as the Prédateurs de Deux Montagnes and the Pierrefonds Marquis. Security was tight; only a handful of designated parents were allowed in the locker rooms.

In the colorfully painted second floor rink, the American flag hung beside Canada's maple leaf. Sitting in my seat overlooking our players' bench, I enjoyed having a bird's-eye view of the team in its private moments. I saw the boys clutching their sticks, heard their whoops and their silences. I watched my son sip his Gatorade through the metal cage of his helmet, wondering what he might be thinking. I saw the coach send the players out onto the ice in split-second timing at strategic moments in the game.

We came home from Canada exhausted, sporting a trophy for our participation and a host of pins traded with other teams. Winning only one out of three games, we never advanced to the finals.

But for weeks, Lucas talked about the experience. He

brought his trophy into school. The team photo taken at the tournament is displayed on our mantle. And on the hat rack hangs the same style of red fleece hockey beret that was part of the signature streetwear of Team Canada at the Olympics. Every time Lucas wears it, I smile. He looks so authentically, well, puckish.

A week after our Canada trip, we packed away the hockey bag and headed for the first practice of the Little League season. There is no travel in bad weather, no 20-pound bag of gear to haul, no blades to continually sharpen, just a glove and cap to grab and go. By the ballfields, mothers sit and gab with each other instead of staying glued to the game. They are not as quick to admonish their sons to play harder, faster, smarter. There is no catchy team cheer.

I watch the kids wind up their fast balls and swing at the bat, but I must admit, there's also none of that gut-grabbing excitement of the rink, none of the vicarious thrill or the intensity of being part of a select group that auditioned for their starring roles.

The other day I checked the calendar. Only 22 more weeks until hockey season.

Robin Springer

Pickup Hockey

Home for Thanksgiving. I wash dishes, standing at my mother's kitchen sink, and shiver. It's windy. A cold draft leaks in around the window. There's no snow on the ground yet, but the temperature's about 16 degrees. I look down across the lot and Scott's pond is deep slate gray, reflecting the low, dark, early winter sky. Mom stood at this window every day while we were growing up, watching the neighborhood kids play ball in the lot in summers and skate on the pond in winters. Nobody plays there now.

There used to be plenty of kids playing. We were like a set of stair-steps. Everybody had a counterpart in another family, matched by age or gender. Tall, lanky, moccasined David, throwing back his head, laughing his purely delighted laugh, and jock Mike, who hunted and trapped with him. Quiet bespectacled Bob and sweet, beautiful John. Debbie, also known as D-Bra, and Molly, whose wheat-blond hair and angel face hid her sturdy tenacity. Geeky, know-it-all Donny, skinny Scotty, the bows of his glasses attached to the frames with wads of white adhesive tape, and rugged little Andy. Derrick and Darryl, Eagle Scout twins, were a pair to themselves, and then I was kind of in between, the girl-poet. There was always somebody to play with, winter or summer.

We were the kids who belonged to a confederation of families living in a neighborhood just inside Trumansburg's village limits, hooked up to municipal services, but a mile from the center of town. The Springers and Scotts lived in rambling houses across from each other on two corners of

Falls Road in a protected spot where Falls and Cemetery Roads intersect. The Polces lived about a quarter of a mile down Cemetery road on a large wooded property that had a creek running through it. Our yards were strewn with barns and sheds and gardens and trees and woodpiles. Grove Cemetery lies peaceful and serene across Cemetery Road from our house. Dad used to say you couldn't ask for quieter neighbors. We laughed painfully "Oh, Dad !" every time he said, "People are dying to get in!" An abandoned Gothic brick chapel (renovated by the Rotarians) with wide cement front steps stands sentry on the cemetery's corner across from our house, and a deep pocket of woods, Smith Woods, shelters the fourth corner. Falls Road starts behind our house in a dead end at Scotts' pond, then meanders east through fields and state land down the mountain to Cayuga Lake.

We had everything we needed right there on that dead end between corner and pond. We were never in the house, except to eat, which we thought about when Mrs. Scott stepped out on her back porch and rang her triangle to gather the troops. We rode bikes up and down the dead end and in the cemetery without worrying about cars or traffic. We bounded through Smith Woods, tripping over tangled myrtle, swerving around, jumping over, fallen logs. Basketballs thudded on asphalt under a hoop attached to Scotts' barn. We never had a bored moment. We played, we sometimes argued. Somebody would get mad and go home, and then twenty minutes later come back to play again as though nothing had happened.

We didn't swim in the pond, since the water was murky and none too clean, but it was perfect for skating. By Thanksgiving, we had to put on our heavy outside clothes to play outside. The older kids wore long underwear and two pairs of jeans with their heavy jackets and assorted ski caps and striped scarves, and the younger kids looked like inflated midgets in red and green and navy blue snowmobile suits. We slid downhill in Scotts' lot while ice on the pond froze thicker and thicker. Pulling with our heels, we slid slowly through heavy, wet, knee-deep snow, packing it with our butts into a slick path around either side of a tree that stood right in the middle. We slid downhill all day long with chapped lips, chapped cheeks, and chapped wrists. Standing back from the slight incline with sleds clasped to chests, we ran to the brink, flung down the sleds and belly-flopped, falling off in a heap at the bottom. Two kids on big round aluminum saucers, legs intertwined, clung to its sides as two others, bent at the waist and digging hard, pushed to get them started down. The saucer spun crazily downhill, veering off the path. We trudged, floundering, pulling suddenly heavy sleds back up the hill, making sure to swerve way out around the sledding paths. Standing at the top, panting, we ate the pea-sized ice balls that clung to the wool hairs of our mittens.

By Christmas the pond was frozen with hard, thick, rough ice, not just a skim coat. December in the Finger lakes was one very cold day after the other, when temperatures never climbed out of the teens, and even colder nights of zero and below, hard freezing-over cold. Leaving your warm house, stepping outside, the sharp cold burned the inside of your nose and it ached a tight pain that made your nose run and your eyes water. Dry, fluffy snow, ever crystal distinct, squeaked and crunched underfoot.

Mr. Scott didn't say much, but he was firm. Nobody was allowed on the ice until it was six inches thick, no matter how anxious we kids were to get out there. Lined up along the pond's edge with out Christmas skates, laces tied together in drooping bows, slung over our shoulders, we waited for the verdict. He cautiously stepped out onto the blue-gray, creaking ice and broke a hole with a metal bar to measure it. Six inches thick!

We swarmed over an old backless wooden bench, pushing, cramming in, tossing skates into a pile. "Get *off* me!" "Move, Mike!" "Will you guys get out of the way?" We all wore figure skates with wide blades and serrated tips, because none of us knew how to skate, or stop, on hockey skates, except for David, who had a fancy pair of skates with long curved blades. Pulling off our mittens to fumble with the knots in our skate laces, and they were always knotted, somehow, fingers instantly began to stiffen and freeze. Sometimes the lace would break and it'd have to be re-laced, one hole at a time, fingers stuck in your armpits to warm them up. We pulled off our boots and perched, five or six kids teetering around the bench's edge, feet in the air, pawing through piles of skates and mittens, yanking one skate after the other out of the mishmash and throwing them back onto the pile till we finally got the right ones. You didn't want to put your feet, or even just a toe, down to balance yourself and get your socks wet in the trampled snow. Our feet ached with cold by the time we glided onto the ice.

Then we were ready to move snow. Sometimes, after the pond froze, if there were inches and inches of snow on it, Mr. Scott drove his lawn tractor down and plowed, but mostly snow got moved with a big snow shovel he rigged up for us kids to use which was a piece of sheet metal nailed between two 2x4's to make a blade. Two kids, pushing hard, scraped snow to the edges of the pond into banks for boundaries. Once in a while the blade caught on lumps or cracks in the ice and sent its pushers flying forward; otherwise kids only stopped pushing when they smashed into a snowbank. It took most of the morning sometimes to push that thing around to clear the snow.

By the time we got a rink shoveled off that was big enough for all of us to skate on, we were all tired out, skated for a half hour and felt frozen to death. Morning snow fell lightly through the sunshine in three or four brief, fierce flurries, but by afternoon most days the sky got low and gray-black clouds moved in. Snow fell thick and fast, heavy enough to cover the ground with a new layer. We whirled around and around, sticking out our tongues to catch the flakes, skating in a cocoon of white and cold and quiet.

One day some of the guys started nudging a stone around the ice with sticks. Never mind that no one knew the rules of ice hockey - at first the games mostly were chucking everybody into the snow or playing keep-away with the "puck." A game was in progress every day; as we gathered at the pond to skate, we just joined up with whichever side needed an extra person. Time went by and the game started to become very committed, very serious, so Dad made a trip – on a Sunday! – to Woolworth's in Ithaca to buy sticks and pucks so we could really play.

Standing at the sink now, I can see Dad – we nicknamed him Gray Eagle – push his knit cap up off his eyes. It glows in the overcast afternoon light. Mom knitted it for him for Christmas using a vivid variegated red, black, white and gray yarn, but her sizing was off and the cap is way too big. Gray Eagle pushes it back up again, crouching slightly, looking deep into the eyes of his opponent, tapping his stick in tight back and forth motions on rough blue-gray ice. He is breathing hard through slightly open mouth, flushed with sweat and cold, damp hair stuck to his forehead. Donny, who is always sent away to be goalie – "Donny, you go down there" – skates around aimlessly behind him in the goal, an indentation chopped into the snowbank with the sharp edge of a snowshovel.

Across from Gray Eagle, five or six kids hunker over, poised, waiting to whack the puck into motion. Someone tosses the puck down, "Alright, GO!", it spins on its edge before falling over and sliding away. Kids jump into motion, pushing off, skating wildly in all directions, sticks waving in the air. The older guys actually try to play hockey, passing the puck back and forth to each other as they glide toward the goal. Suddenly Molly darts in and smacks the puck hard. It bounces off Donny, who wasn't watching, hurtles past Debbie, figure skating in her corner, and ricochets off the snowbank back into the thick of the skaters. Dad reaches over our heads into the confusion, gains control and handles the puck, slapping it gently back and forth in front of him as he zooms around the pond, jukin' and jivin', "And Gray Eagle gains control! He's a magician! No one can catch the amazing Gray Eagle!", dazzling around us while we all stand there with our mouths hanging open. A mob of us chases after him, slicing and hacking with our sticks, legs and skates tangled.

Suddenly Andy somehow nabs the puck and zooms away with it. Hockey sticks fly down the ice – we throw them, "Stop the puck!" because we can't catch up with the guy! "It's a free-for all! The game is a regular melee!" Gray Eagle is shouting, jumping "Go! Go! You've got it! Score!". The puck disappears in a morass of legs and sticks, and Andy goes down – tripped by a gang of people determined to get that puck away from him.

There is blood all over. We're all yelling, "Oh, my God!" "What happened?" "Andy, you all right, man?" but still looking crazily, madly around for the puck, which is nowhere to be seen. Andy stands up, a little dazed, and wipes at his ear. Somehow, in this very crazy accident, it flopped over and somebody, maybe Bobby, maybe John, skated over the back of it. Then, in the way of kids, the bloodier it is, the funnier it is, and we are laughing, *laughing,* skating over to inspect the injury, laughing and exclaiming

“Gross!” “Oh, *man*!” Scotty laughs his wild hyena laugh, falling over with glee.

Until we hear a yelping shout from the goal. And there stands Donny, clutching his forehead where he has gotten smacked with the puck, while Dad skates in an oblivious victory dance, arms overhead, yelling “No one stops the amazing Gray Eagle!”

Marion M. Rapp

Center Ice

White jerseyed skaters, silver blades flashing
Cut hard ice, chips fly.
Bodies weave, flowing following
A black blur. The puck skims
Over white ice, passed crisply
Thunks on sticks, bangs off boards.

Watchful and wary, the goalie guards
Against rocket pucks, slap-shot
From forwards, streaking swiftly
Near his net. They shoot, he saves.

Back up the ice, the other way
We watch the devil's dance
Storm through the lines and score.

Nils Clausson

Breakaway Sonnet

… at 19:20 the harassed centre
loses, ineptly, the rebellious puck
to the alert just turning defenceman
stickhandles beside around the caught off-

guard left-wing and fluid as a dancer's
leap eludes crosses spots his breaking right-
wing draws it in as if on a taut string
streaks to the last defender then backhands

to his own alone (as if in a field
of summer wheat) defenceman bursts goalward
feints with head and hips making the goalie
commit himself too soon he shoots he scores

and turns arms high to the cheering hearts stirred
in the place where the poem has occurred.

David Bengtson

A Drink

When ice finally stretched across
ponds and swamp in the hollow
behind the Lutheran cemetery
and thickened to hold even
our most tentative steps,

the hockey games began.
Every night after school
teams were quickly chosen.
Only an hour to play
before dark.

Between hunks of wood
marking the goals at each end
stood the two worst players.
Someone always brought a puck
with initials carved
carefully and deep.

Then the call,
"We'll bring it up,"
as the best skater on that team
cradled puck against black blade
and began the races
to the other end.

The clatter of sticks,
the slash of blades into ice
echoed across the hollows,
rose to the cemetery
where even in winter
young couples walked and kissed –

where, in summer, they made love
hidden by tall grass, bouquets of dead flowers,
and scores of scarred slate gravestones –
where we, once, hiding flat
on the roof of the custodian's shack,
watched, wide-eyed and quiet.

At the end of the game,
when puck became shadow,
we hammered the butt ends of our sticks
through the ice to make
holes big enough for a drink.

At any other time of year
we thought it crazy to drink
swamp water with its green
screen of scum and bugs.
Only rocks, sticks, a turtle or snake
broke that opaque surface.

But in winter, weary after the sweat of hockey,
we stretched out on our pocked pond
and in the grey light
sipped from this muddy bowl
the most delicious dark water of all.

Adam Berlin

Cup Check

School nights we slapped the puck around.
Four boards around a dirt lot.
Hosed down when the cold came.
Bumpy over tufts of grass, a stray rock.

No lifting the puck.
Skates and Sticks our only equipment.
Bent and taped – perfect.

Playing our parts.
Wayne Cashman. Stan Jonathan.
Terry O'Reilly. He's the best fighter.
Most penalty minutes.

My feet went numb only
when the skates came off.
Balled hands in gloves.
Finger parts floppy.
Frozen snot.
Air whistled when I closed my mouth,
breathed in.

Walking through woods back
to Chestnut Street. Hockey talk.
Hip checks into snow drifts.
Slap in the balls. Cup check.

Boston Garden Dis man tled.

Time Difference. Inevitable like
a rink break. The Zamboni man
responsibly smoothing over chips
and cuts.

Winter comes and clocks
are changed and work goes into
night and office heating, fluorescent
lights take my energy, tripping me
up.
No ice to drop gloves on.
No boards to slap pucks at.
The sound of hard rubber
hitting wood so right, leaving
my mark.

Justin Bryant

Hakkanen's Move

Until he saw Rikard Hakkanen's new move, things were going well for Doug Kazlor. In just his second season he'd established himself as one of the Continental Hockey Association's most respected enforcers, a "team" player who always stood up for his teammates when games turned sour. In addition to his fighting skills, opposing defensemen found his hulking frame almost impossible to move from in front of the net, and in a half-season he'd picked up four goals – not a bad total, considering he didn't get much more than a handful of shifts per game.

Most true enforcers have a flaw or two in their game. Doug's was skating. He worked on it diligently, staying after practice day after day to weave through cones set up by Keith McManus, the Raleigh Flyboys' assistant coach. But although he'd improved some from his rookie year, he still couldn't get his 6'5" body to change direction with any certainty. He was a victim of momentum.

So he fought, and he checked, and he skated through his cones. He made $1400 a month, which seemed like a fortune to him. His rent was meager – $320 for a small but clean one bedroom apartment, discounted because the landlord was a season ticket holder. He saved money by not owning a car. No payment, no insurance, no repairs, no gas. That's what he told his teammates. The truth was that for all his toughness on the ice, Doug Kazlor hated cars and was afraid to drive. His teammates gave him rides to practice or, more often, he took the bus. It was an uncomplicated life.

He did his best not to think about the NHL, about the money that even tough guys could make up there. He considered it an unhealthy distraction.

Doug had rarely played with or against European players until he joined the Flyboys. Raleigh had only one, a 19-year-old Finn named Rikard Hakkanen. He was tall, lean and fast, with quick feet and soft hands. He was part of the new breed of Europeans, who understood that North American hockey was physical. Rikard didn't mind chasing pucks into the corner, even though he knew it meant getting drilled. He was a good stickhandler who liked to carry the puck, and because of that he drew hits all over the ice. Some of them were cheap, which kept Doug busy. During games Doug never sat down. He stood in front of his bench, watching behind the puck to see if any opponent took liberties with his teammates. When they did, Doug didn't have to be told what to do. He had eighteen fighting majors to go with his four goals.

One other thing about Rikard Hakkanen: he could skate. Oh, how he could skate! Before practice he would weave complex patterns around the creamy ice, slowly increasing speed, his strides long and sure with no wasted motion.

"Like the Bushmen of Africa," he told his teammates. "They can run fast all day, they know how to use their energy. I saw it on Discovery Channel."

Doug watched Rikard skate. He pretended to stretch along the boards, but he'd be watching Rikard skate his patterns, listening to the cool snick-snick of his blades as he whisked past. Doug thought the sight of Rikard Hakkanen skating was beautiful. He told Keith McManus that once. Keith had laughed at him.

The Flyboys were working on their power play one day in

practice when they first saw Rikard's new move. Rikard was on the point, and Doug was filling in on the kill team, only because three regulars were out with the flu. They defended the power play deep. Doug wanted to challenge the puck, but Barry Martin, the head coach, liked to keep the box low.

"Let them pass around us, never through!" he shouted.

The makeshift kill team was doing a good job. Doug used his enormous reach to intercept several passes and sling them the length of the ice. He whooped happily and taunted the power play unit. Barry Martin interrupted the practice to correct mistakes several times. Rikard Hakkanen looked angry. Several of his sublime passes jostled off the sticks of his less-skilled teammates. He growled in Finnish.

The next time he got the puck at the point he drew his stick back to shoot and then held it there, inviting a challenge. Doug forced himself to wait, but then heard Barry Martin yelling something he couldn't quite make out. He rushed at the puck and swiped at it with his stick – it was *right there* in front of him – and then it was gone, and Rikard Hakkanen was gone. He saw first the front and then the back of his jersey in a blur, then turned and stumbled as the slender Finn walked in on goal and rang a quick wrister off the crossbar. The players were impressed, but too cool to show it. Barry Martin stopped practice again.

"Let's see that one more time," he said.

Rikard shrugged. He faked a slapper, swung his blade over the puck, then drew it back with his backhand and pirouetted a tight 180-degree turn, pulling the puck with him as he spun. Doug had seen the move before – a grainy replay from the 60's or 70's, Bobby Hull maybe – but he'd never seen anyone do it in person. The other players tried it. They were so slow in the turn it was clear it would never fool anyone in a real game.

To Rikard Barry said, "If you're gonna try that in a game, it better work. If any of the rest of you try it, it's a hundred dollar fine."

Doug said, "Well run me a tab, Barry, because I'm gonna *own* that move."

Everyone laughed, even Rikard, and Doug felt good. He knew his teammates appreciated and liked him. It was the best part of his job. It was why he didn't mind the fighting.

. . .

With four minutes left in the first period against Wilkes-Barre, Doug got his first shift. He backchecked, helped free the puck in the corner, and chased after it when it was cleared. The referee stopped play on a high stick. Before the neutral zone face-off one of the Wilkes-Barre forwards cruised past him and said, "Hey mister tough guy, they finally let you on the ice?"

Doug recognized him. It was Frank Stonewald, an aging enforcer who'd played for at least a half-dozen minor league teams. They'd fought earlier in the season. Doug had been getting the better of it, but the linesmen broke it up early. "Next time, junior, you're dead!" Stonewald had shouted, a purple mouse already rising under his left eye. Doug had said nothing. He didn't like to talk on the ice.

Stonewald lined up opposite him for the face-off. Doug gave him his best enforcer's glare. "I figured you'd be selling cars by now," Stonewald said, breathing hard. Doug turned his head and waited for the face-off. He knew they weren't going to fight yet. He'd just come on the ice, while Stonewald was finishing a long shift and was gassed. That was one of the unwritten Tough Guy Rules: don't square off with a guy who's at the end of a shift. Doug took it seriously, along with other maxims such as no headbutting, no sucker punches and no jumping non-fighters, unless they're asking for it. From what he'd heard around the league, Frank Stonewald didn't always abide by the Tough Guy Rules. But even if that were so, Doug wasn't lowering himself to cross that line.

When the puck dropped Stonewald skated to his bench. A few minutes later, just before the end of the period, Doug heard his name being called from the home bench. It was Frank Stonewald. "Next period," Stonewald mouthed, then waggled his fists and smiled.

"Whatever you say, grandpa," Doug said. Stonewald was always talking. It annoyed him.

Doug got more ice time in the second, but Stonewald never left the bench and Doug soon forgot about him. The ice was rutty and chipped, and he was having a hard time with the puck. "Fighting it," as Barry sometimes said. He had a great chance to score when the Wilkes-Barre goalie left a bad rebound right at his feet, but he chopped at the puck and it fluttered wide.

"Don't beat it to death!" Barry said to him on the bench.

On his next shift he got on the end of another rebound. This time he steadied his skates and swept a smooth, quick wrist shot to the blocker side. It hissed past the goalie and - *ting!* - smacked squarely off the crossbar and bounced to safety.

"That's the way to shoot, sniper!" Keith McManus said. "You're focused now. Things'll happen."

But Barry left him on the bench for most of the rest of the second period. Then Stonewald, in a rare shift, took a run at Rikard and cross checked him in the back of the neck. The Flyboys scored on the power play to take a 3-0 lead. When Stonewald went back on the ice, Barry said, "Doug, go."

Sometimes somebody had to fight. It was part of the game. He wouldn't claim to love fighting, but he didn't mind. It was his job, and he knew he was good at it. When he lined up against Stonewald, he knew why Barry had sent him out. But he was still thinking about his two missed scoring chances.

"Guess it's go time," Stonewald said, but for once Doug didn't seem to hear him.

The puck dropped. Doug waited for the automatic responses to take over – to drop his gloves and fling his stick far behind him, where it couldn't get in the way, to let the other guy throw the first punch or two while he lunged and grabbed onto his sleeves, to free his right hand and start throwing it and throwing it – but none of that happened. He saw the puck and he took off after it, leaving Stonewald standing with his gloves half-off. Doug caught up to the puck in the corner, dug it out, and headed for the crease. Rikard lashed a shot from the point. Doug followed it easily, as if it were moving in slow motion. He raised his stick and tipped it ever so slightly. The puck thudded into the goalie's chest, and he covered the rebound. The small crowd cheered.

Another missed chance, but this time he felt good about it. Two of his teammates skated by and tapped him with their sticks, and Steve Previn, the Flyboys' captain, shouted "Good stuff Dougie!" from the bench.

Stonewald seemed less impressed. The Wilkes-Barre goon looked at him with a mixture of confusion and disgust, then headed towards his bench. "I gotta job to do, but nobody wants to dance!" he shouted, loud enough for Doug to hear.

Doug's ice time was steady into the third period. Wilkes-Barre had nobody who could handle him down low, but he still found himself fighting the puck from time to time. The ice had been bad enough early in the game, but by the middle of the third it was soft as well as rutty. Doug could almost feel his skate blades sinking into the slush with every stride. He wondered why it didn't seem to be bothering anybody else.

He didn't know exactly why he hadn't fought Stonewald earlier. He'd been in a sort of fog then, brooding over his missed chances. Now he was distracted by the sloppy ice, by Stonewald's incessant yapping from the bench, by the ache in his legs as his inefficient strides sapped his energy. With six minutes to play he gathered a loose puck at the left face-off circle. He had space, but the puck clattered off his stick yet again. A Wilkes-Barre defenseman rushed at him. Doug corralled the puck. He heard a teammate calling for it at the blue line. He knew he should drop it to him, or wrap it behind the net. Keep it moving. That's what Barry was always saying. But he did neither. He saw the defenseman grasping for the puck, saw that he was off balance, vulnerable. He had a sudden, absurd thought – "This is the perfect time for Rikard's move! – and he believed it.

It didn't work. The defensman clipped him as he was spinning. The puck squirted free. Wilkes-Barre almost had an odd-man rush, but a backchecking Flyboy managed to break it up. Doug skated to the bench for a line change. Stonewald was laughing and yelling at him from the Wilkes-Barre bench. Barry glared at him but said nothing. His teammates didn't look at him at all. Keith McManus sidled up to him.

"You're fine, you're fine," he said.

"I know."

"Look, stay within your limits, okay? Even Rikard doesn't have that move down, and he *invented* it. Play your game, not his."

Doug nodded. But he didn't get another shift that night. When the game ended he went out to his goalie with his teammates, then turned and shuffled towards the locker room. The Wilkes-Barre players were crossing in front of him. He saw Stonewald looking at him. Just what I need now, he thought.

"Hey Kazlor," Stonewald said casually as he passed. "If you feel like doing your job tomorrow, look me up. I guess now you know you aren't too good to fight." Then he laughed. "What the *hell* was that move he was trying, anyway?" he said loudly to his teammates.

"See, that's what is so great about these home-and-home games," Keith said as they clumped down the tunnel. "If you have a bad game or make a mistake, you've only got to wait twenty-four hours for redemption. You can fix problems before they settle in. That way you stay out of slumps."

Doug nodded. "Yeah, you're right," he said. He watched Stonewald troop into his locker room.

He thought, be seeing you soon, Frank.

Peter Desy

My Father's Picture on the Cover of a Buffalo Bison's Hockey Program for 1934

Booze took him from me
when I was too young
to understand, before his real death
in 1979. In this picture
he is about 25. The caption reads
"Speedy Desy, a Rising Star."
I remember when I was small
he passed the puck to me
on the ice rink in the park.
I was pumping wildly, reaching
for his pass. It hit my stick
perfectly, and I've never felt so whole
as then – skating fast on the flat earth,
the wind at our backs, sailing
off the edge at full speed,
never landing, my arms around
his neck, the big stars
everywhere, all around us.

Anna A. Hillen

Very Thin Ice

The poets tell us that April is the cruellest month but we know that December can be just as cruel since it's the month of Christmas, a time when the separated, the grieving, and the poor are made most aware of their plight. Yet the glossy catalogues and magazines have always told us Christmas is a time of plenty, togetherness, celebration, even out-and-out hedonism.

I suppose my family's Christmas of 1950 was mostly cruel with a mini-dose of togetherness as the only element from that other alien world of bounty and beneficence. My father had died the previous March and had been buried on a brutally wet and windy day. My mother was still coming to grips with the reality of her physical loss: financially, we had already lost just about all we could. The furniture was sparse and very worn; the floors clean but bare and cold; the pantry shelves close to empty.

I had turned fifteen in October; my brother had been ten since July. We were more than old enough to know our situation was severe and to know to keep to ourselves most of our hopes and desires for Christmas time. Still, a ten year old child, a Canadian boy **has** to play hockey – *some* kind of hockey. Street hockey is O.K. in the fall, in and out of the Dodges, Studebakers and Nashes parked tight to the inner city curbs. Any projectile for a puck: a tennis ball, a piece of coal, a square of wood from a neighbouring handy man, maybe even a real puck but not often because they cost fifteen cents at Woolworth's and went down the back opening on the street sewers before you could wink and in spite of all attempts at a Sawchuck save.

But when the mercury plummets and the boards go up at the not-too-nearby park, then ice hockey is the only game in town. Clothes didn't matter back then. Any patched and chewed apparel was acceptable. Shin pads, chest pads and helmets were either unheard of or worn only by pros. But you had to have skates.

And so in our ever-so-humble home in mid-November my brother's cry went out: "Geez, I hope Santa brings me skates, real hockey skates." As the days passed, the queries became more frequent, insistent, and specific. "Santa Claus will know to bring me black skates, won't he? With waxed yellow laces? Oh, and steel toes?"

I don't remember exactly how mother and I found the money for the boots, blades and laces. I put in almost all my babysitting money and somehow she found the rest. I elected to negotiate with the men at the Dunne's Skate factory at the top of our street, a block away. The skate factory was the only benefit to life on our particular inner city street, interrupted as it was by rundown corner stores, a dry cleaners, a linseed oil factory and a very noisy quadruple line of train tracks. A straight-from-the-factory purchase meant a lower price. I suspected an over-the-counter personal sob story from a loving sister might mean an even lower price. And I was right. So, it was mid-December and we had the skates, in the box, hidden on the shelf above the cellar stairs.

Then another detail was added to the plea for skates, "Would Santa remember to include tendon guards?" Mother and I rolled our eyes wildly. What, in the name of all that's holy or probably unholy, were tendon guards? I went forth again – to Maher's Shoes on Queen Street. "Do you have tendon guards for hockey skates?" I asked casually with the bravado that comes naturally to most teenagers experienced by now at bluffing, after years of practicing on school teachers. I remember they were $1.75 each though the skate price has vanished. Home again for the skates and then to the shoe repair shop on Fuller Avenue to have Pete stitch the guards onto the skate backs. No one-piece modular tubular whatevers back then. "Very nize skates. Ver you get zem?" I glowed with pride and toted them back to their hidey-hole above the cellar stairs.

A few days before Christmas they were wrapped in sheets of gift wrap left over from better days. "FROM SANTA WITH LOVE" was printed on a square of white note pad. During all the passing days Mother and I had been treated repeatedly to the same chorus of details, all of which we could recite resignedly under our breath: hockey skates, black leather, yellow laces, waxed, tendon guards, and, as an afterthought, "The Christmas cards always show Santa with his sacks of toys: dolls, bears, books, trucks, and stuff. He doesn't have time to make everything and wrap it too, does he? "I suppose not..." my mother sighed. Late Christmas Eve we took off the gift wrap and note; left the skates in the open box near the fireplace; moved back the fireplace screen; sprinkled coal dust swept up from the coal pile in the basement; left a half glass of milk and some cookie crumbs, and tiptoed off to bed.

I can't remember anything else about that Christmas: what Mother and I received, what else – if anything – we gave to others. But "wee Davey" had his skates – from Santa, the Santa in whom he had to believe, as his only hope.

Dale Jacobs

Shinny

Days of shinny, we played pick up games far into the night
until our feet were numb, toes feeling like they would snap off,
fingers rubbing through socks soaked with sweat, kneading
the feeling back, ready for another period in the never ending
game past the moment's break.

Spring when the ice got slushy, bumps grew along the boards
where water dripped from the metal roof, deep winter when ice
was burned to a ghostly white, hard, unforgiving, knees, elbows
bruised to a fine black, shavings rising from stopping skates,
a delicious arc of ephemera.

Half-cylinder of corrugated steel, oversize machine shop becomes
a rink, men of the town coming in from the field, tractors giving
way to hammers and saws and arc welders, coming together for
us, for skating, for games of hockey on cold Canadian winter
nights that seemed to last forever.

Sitting in this southern town, no nights cold enough to frost your
moustache, I wonder if anyone knows who built our rink or what it
meant, if anyone skates or plays hockey long into the night, giving
themselves over to the game, surrendering to air thick with cold,
breath suspended for just a moment.

Ronn Hartviksen

Making Olympic Ice (When the Olympic Team Laced Up In Our Backyard)

Looking back over eighteen seasons at the Bean Pot, where snowy winters have engulfed our rural rink, one recalls encounters with some very interesting creatures who have left impressions on our frozen stage. These include bear, moose, deer, foxes, wolves, and porcupines. Plus exceptional varieties of migrating birds including woodland hawks, owls, and even resident flying squirrels. Yet our fondest human visitors arrived after a series of wintry weeks in the winter of 1987. Now, as I write, this story seems as fresh as the calligraphy ink of yesterday drying on the surface of today's open journal.

. . .

It was merely a month before the opening of the World's Winter Olympics in Calgary, Alberta. And, while the Canadian Olympic team was making its way across North America playing exhibition matches leading up to the Olympic games, we were alerted by *Hockey Night In Canada* (HNIC) that we might be a potential site for a scrimmage session. The plan was to produce a film to promote the game of shinny and recreational hockey.

The region around Thunder Bay by late November, and early December, is traditionally cold enough to promote open air ice for outdoor skating. So plans were tentatively arranged to have the Olympic team play on our rink when their touring schedule brought them to our town during the Christmas holidays. By contrast, other locations in the

Maritimes or Calgary with its chinook winds or the temperate conditions in British Columbia could not guarantee steady freezing temperatures required to make natural ice in a project of this sort.

As a family when we advanced this proposal little did we realize what bitterly cold, and, extremely unusual weather would precede our willingness to accommodate these Olympians.

There is a blissful state I've always enjoyed as a rink rat in making outdoor ice. Uncoil the lines, turn on the water, and gleefully begin going about spraying every inch of the rink. Gradually, as if by magic, ice crystallization takes hold on a mirrored nordic court. A perfect medium for skaters. I find a rhythm in these watering sessions especially when longer nights, with plummeting temperatures, lock us into winter. It's also a great time to think. Without a single mosquito invading your thoughts. It's an idyllic winter think-tank especially when things are flowing neatly.

However, back then, as December roared in the mercury sank so quickly, and consistently, into sub-zero temperatures (-20 to -26 F) our exterior faucet froze solid. This was major hoar-frosting. At the base of the waterline our homemade cast-iron spigot was being swallowed in massive ice formations serrated like fangs. The shutoff valve with its copper petals peeked through transparent layers of ice: the image of a rusty flower unable to bloom. Suspended in archeological ice resembling amber. Everything denying access to running water: the lifeline in ice making. I resorted to a blow torch in thawing and regaining mobility for fresh floodings. I also identified with the philosophical observation Jacques Maritain leaves us on "the feelings of a primitive man looking at the all-pervading forces of Nature."

After three weeks of being exposed to the elements every day

I had acquired the ultimate in freezer burn on both thumbs and index fingers. Possibly only a mountaineer in the Himalayas would have been as passionately crazy refusing to step out of this raw bleakness, each day, where progress seemed like regress. Up against this kind of testing occasionally made me feel like some absurd character in Samuel Beckett's existential theatre. A frail earthling, alone on an island of ice, once visitors and neighbouring kids had left for their suppers. Here I was wrapped in a tattered parka. Standing in oversized kodiak boots. With a balaclava pulled over my face. Two or three scarves tied around my forehead and neck with only my eyes squinting through a marginal space. By the second hour of each shift, my eyelashes were almost welded together in the extremes of -30 degrees. I wore a pair of very thermal (though very weathered) Mackinaw trousers pulled over long johns. My hands were constantly freezing, inside of liners and leather mitts, feebly guiding the hose as the flooding stuttered along.

Excessive use of our rubber hosing resulted in pin-hole leaks – mostly at the connections, though occasionally elsewhere – and the hose spewed like a sieve in every direction. Wildly. Everywhere. Now the flow of water had a secondary tributary. Fsszzzst! It sounded spreading wickedly upwards all over me, and, even higher into the ink black sky. When I came in after each flooding my leggings had virtually frozen into thick boards caked in ice. Like fishmonger slabs I hung them on hooks by the steps to the cellar near the wood furnace. They took til the next day to drip dry.

Blowing warmth on my hands by the fireplace one night, an American friend commented, "have you ever thought of insuring your hands? Musicians do."

I felt dumb. Numb. Reduced. And, a bit touched. Nothing but a naive heart totally in love with a game called hockey. A crazy Canuck ice-making madness had washed over me. This went well beyond any civilized definition, slipping into a conversation, about how to gauge one's participation in winter activities inside of trying conditions. At the same time at outdoor rinks–operated by the city–under-scored signs were posted saying: "Too cold to-night. See what to-morrow brings."

With the last week of ice preparation nearly upon us, and, while deliberately attempting to defy mother Nature's bleak conditions I remember another cluster of trying days, with vicious winds, where it seemed all the gods of the Hockey Hall of Fame were trying to force this rendez-vous with Team Canada into an indoor location. Back in 1907, the poet Robert Service had painted a gruesome portrait of Sam McGee, up in the Yukon, who I reckoned could not have been much colder before asking someone to close the door on what seemed like McGee's arctic re-enactment. We were more than halfway through a freezing odyssey; there had to be an oasis of warmth lingering somewhere, I mused.

But as our last days of preparation were evaporating the on-going re-surfacing necessitated a little work at leveling low spots. (This is the part in ice making that reminds me of a groundskeeper's fine techniques working the greens at a golf course.) My son Galen, age 14, and I brought in snow from the surrounding woods using a wheelbarrow. Galen had been my best co-assistant throughout these compelling days when he was free from school and his saxophone practices. We used small hand shovels and gingerly spread patches of white snow onto the much darker ice surface where little dips, or valleys, were imminent. We sprinkled the mix using watering cans which we had filled inside at a laundry tub and then tamped these new quilts of ice into the overall mosaic. We simply refused to open up the waterlines taxing our water supply with this quotidian chore.

At night, winds still scowled. Trees actually cracked open rupturing their outer bark. Often the haze of Northern Lights dancing across the horizon seemed much colder within this landscape than we had ever experienced before. But, to me, there was an unexpected revelation in finding an intrepid and affirmative spirit oozing from this adventure. And, I must admit, there were some particularly warm embers of inspiration beginning to be kindled about me.

It may have been something as sweet as the first stars sprayed so brightly onto the backdrop of those final nights. I recall stars blinking ever so kindly over the western horizon where moments before one felt the impulse to call it quits and book off. Inexplicable how the distant energy of a twinkling star often kept the work going for another three-quarters of an hour or so. "A far flung strew of stars," as Joseph Brodsky might have put it, burning with a cordial warmth like little campfires of energy in a rarified sky.

Besides, there was the daily arrival of chickadees chirping their little songs. Their delightful movement and flickering flight paths accompanied choral tunes sounding such hope near our feeding station. One night, between shifts, I was watching a re-run of *The Bird Man of Alcatraz* on TV when I realized what it was about birds being able to draw one out of a little depression. They are adapters. Survivors of the fiercest elements. Creatures able to build homes without the use of arms. And when things are looking up, they resort to music to accent life's comings and goings. On my next shift, I pulled out a few extension lines and a tape recorder and played Handel's *Water Music* as I attempted another flooding. It was musical medicine to the soul. Until the tape froze and suddenly stopped. Alas. Handel's river of music had iced over. I turned out the lights. Then moved all our gear, and audio inspiration, to the mouth of the wood chute door.

I crawled inside. Dragged the lines through an opening, and, remember only a basement full of hosing entangled like lengths of green spaghetti. Every bit of hosing covered in ice that crackled like a frozen whip no matter how gently I positioned it. Nothing to work with now. Things had to thaw. Time also to get some sleep. It was 3:15 am.

Weaving through this there was the eternal thawing thought operating on my mind that this freezer chest of weather simply had to break up and would someday be carted away by a warming front.

After thirty-two consecutive days a miracle plot of ice was rather nicely emerging with only a week to go. But as our timeline drew near, another cold front set in from the prairies where fifty-year-old record temperatures were shattered. Our ice cracked painfully each time fresh water spilled out from the hose. I thought of the chemists of ancient Greece who thought ice was a crystal formation like quartz. A crystal as solid as rock in the building blocks of minerals making up their knowledge in the classical world of alchemy.

One morning, at the end of that week as the first rays of sunlight appeared, the Bean Pot glistened. Our work had evolved into something like a giant cake pan of ice. Our rectangular corral of whitewashed wooden walls 60' x 101' (in size) were made of 4' x 8' recycled plywood with candy apple red dashers. We had attached high wire screening running the lengths of space behind either goal. The goals were humble. Two homemade hockey nets built with 2" x 4" s using stitched gunny sacks for netting. All was set to go.

Coiling the hose and heading to the cellar to prepare for our special hockey guests, I recalled Emerson's "the mark of wisdom is to see the miraculous in the common." Then I tripped as I made my way down the steps and fell. As I stumbled with the garden hose unwinding away from me, I instantly felt the uncommonness of a common man so awkwardly brittle with cold. I was tumbling with less agility than an astronaut, burdened with all the insular gear worn on a moon walk, wobbling around in space trying to reel in my umbilical cord. This routine had become so much more than the sum of all these hysterical parts seen in retrospect.

In the early morning darkness of the day after Team Canada had played an exhibition game against the Soviets, in Thunder Bay, our phone rang with a call from *Hockey Night In Canada's* Executive Producer, Don Wallace, who had flown in to direct the filming.

"How's the ice," he inquired.

"Just great," I said.

"What's the temperature out there," he asked.

"Well, the thermometer says -17 F," immediately thinking they won't want to be outside in this atmosphere. "But, it's calm and things seem to be warming up," I continued.

"We'll be out with camera equipment shortly. The Olympians will soon follow. See you in a while." He hung up the phone.

When I stepped back outside there were hordes of evening grosbeaks and whiskey jacks warming at the top of the chimney and I thought this day was still slightly more cruel, and less kind, than it need be.

But as the filming unfolded, the Olympians arrived as enthusiastic as pee wee hockey players eager to skate on natural ice in spite of the permafrost still hanging in the air. They laced up in every nook and cranny of our home. Players sat on chairs, stools, and steps going upstairs or down. My wife, Margaret said, "I kept thinking we must be running a motel with everyone either checking in–or out–at the same time. My lord, I couldn't believe the amount of Olympic equipment they had carted up the front steps into our home: gigantic traveling bags, sweat suits, and even toques. Everything so richly embossed. Stamped with the red, blue, and white Team Canada logo. For a long while after I kept seeing as we listened to the anthem before other hockey games that winter."

It didn't take long for the players to move outside. They dashed onto the ice which shone with the texture of marble. Some players wore toques. Others caps. Some had wrapped scarves around their faces. Others played having lifted the hoods of their *Team Canada* warm-up suits over their heads. How quickly everyone got used to the refreshing snap of December on a woodland rink. Fortunately, a redeeming sun penetrated a frozen stand of peripheral trees.

The rest of the morning we raced back and forth playing an east-west game of shinny with friends and neighborhood kids joining us in the making of a film that was eventually called *The Young Olympians* and shown on CBC TV during the Olympics.

"This is what hockey's all about," exclaimed goaltender Sean Burke (currently playing goal with the Philadelphia Flyers of the NHL). He blocked shots with great candor as players meandered liberally through his crease.

"You know I grew up playing ball hockey on the streets of Vancouver where we didn't have outdoor ice like this," said Ken Berry, a free-wheeling winger for Team Canada. "But this is the kind of setting I really would like to have known when I was a kid learning about hockey. It brings out your natural instincts like beavers swimming in a pond. A terrific place to develop stick handling, skating, and shooting techniques. On such a great sheet of open air ice!"

It was amazing to see how quickly everything about this event brought out an inner glow which goes hand-in-hand with living in a polar climate. As muscles and hearts warmed up, the Olympians and kid skaters meshed into a flow. Movements quite naturally adapted within the rhythm of free spirited play. There was a crispness and youthfulness bringing out the best in everyone involved.

"This rink reminds me of the river we skated on in Saskatchewan," said one of the Olympians resting his red-and-white Maple Leaf glove on an entrance gate. "Until today I hadn't thought of that for ages. We travel by planes from airport to airport and then head indoors to play in very modern arenas. But you can be sure I'll be thinking about this place, and our stream in the prairies, on our next plane to a rink."

"It was great getting a few tips from all those Olympic players," commented Jeff Forneri, age 15, one of the youngsters who took part. "When I scored a goal I actually felt I was part of Paul Henderson's winning Canadian Team from the 1972 Summit Series in Moscow. It was a real thrill skating with the guys wearing our country's colors."

"It's from places like this, spread across every winter in Canada, where we find our best brand of hockey players and backyard talents," said assistant coach Tom Watt. "When you drop the puck in a game of shinny it may take you a while to know who your teammates are. But within shinny matches you polish skills needed to enjoy the great tempo of skating and passing emerging in good hockey at any exceptional level of the game."

"There's a romance to this kind of hockey," said Team Canada coach Dave King (now with the coaching staff of the Montreal Canadiens). "A romance kept alive on every patch of barnyard ice, or makeshift rink, where hockey was first cradled. There was also a motto where we grew up, in the West, which went: unless you do the shoveling and maintain the rink, you really can't enjoy the true texture of the ice. Many people attribute this phrase to Vic Stasiuk who played with the Boston Bruins. But a phrase like that," King continued, "is such a fine observation on what keeps open air rinks functioning in all parts of the dominion of Canada and the northern states."

Shortly after this once-in-a-lifetime engagement ended the Olympians drove away to connect with a plane heading east to Quebec. I began shoveling a few sugary heaps of snow over the boards after scraping and then sweeping with a broom. I noticed the weather had turned. The sun was brilliant sinking towards a far horizon. So many birds had reappeared at our feeding station. There was a new ambience hovering. It felt as if a touch of a milder season was embellishing the air. The weather had become balmy. It felt temporarily like a time later in winter, perhaps March. I was comfortable casting off my mitts and working with my bare hands. Skin is a great healer, and, the splits and freezer burn in my hands were passing scars in a production now ending.

We'd come halfway across another winter and met with some measure of triumph following the challenges of the weeks before. It dawned on me we had lived (ever so briefly) inside a line W.H. Auden once wrote. "Think of this day," Auden noted, "as one thinks of a day when one did something slightly unusual."

What a long way we had journeyed from our beginnings as kids who initially skated on frozen creeks, back in time, to this protean scrimmage charting a re-discovery in the origins of our game: hockey.

There was a heartbeat involved that inspired our son to write about what happened. His composition was written a day later.

The cold mist of your breath spurts out as you skate
gracefully down the Bean Pot ice towards the net. Stick
handling perfectly as dreams of all your favourite
Olympic players float through your head. You move to
the left, then to the right, and, back to the left.
Quickly you snap a shot that bubbles up through the
air as it finds the top corner. Scoring the winning goal
in an Olympic Year. You jump into the air jubiliantly
and are caught by your teammates .
These are the dreams I always share with you, Dad, as
we face-off on our rink.

– Galen.

John B. Lee

The Firehall Blues

We cure the firehall blues
with booze.

After we've hung our skates to dry
like ripe skins
we talk about accidents.
Checks,
slashed faces, eyes carved out of skull's knot holes.
One year
Al saw a boy die on the ice
his jugular cut
and pumping red.

But mostly we talk about scoring.
The easy grace
in the best of us
swiveling into perfection
only then
when the puck arcs past a shoulder,
or slides cool and swift
along the ice
to tangle in the netting
like a hard black fish
that darts of its own accord.

We get drunk
on victory
smashed
on defeat
and when we go home to our wives
tired and drained with the telling
of the same stories
in as many ways as we can conjure
we go with the knowledge
that we will pay dearly tomorrow
for the glory
we hooked tonight.

Peter McEwen

Brouhaha

Brouhaha erupts at MASK shouts *Packet headline.*

A colour photo catches the violent crunch of players,
coaches, officials

and fans against the rink's protective glass, as they spill from
ice surface

to dressing room runway like fish from a bowl. The coach
and his son,

the captain... leader only in penalties taken, faces twinned in
rage,

front and centre in the melee, clutch and tear at the
departing winners.

The sports editor on his page calls it a brawl decrying the
sordidness

of the incident which detracted from the heroic performance
of the home team.

Rising to the occasion they had been playing over their heads
against

a more talented and cooler opposition. Then a questionable
penalty in sudden

death overtime lead to the goal, the demise of their hockey
season and

to their unseemly conduct. Clyde, an old time goaler, who
saw it all

in the semi pros, sits in the inner circle, the phallocentric
hub at Sonny's Garage.

He draws on his White Owl, lowers the paper and speaks through a cloud

of smoke *it wasn't even a good f'n donnybrook ... it was just*

plain dumb ugly. Decorum prohibits rough language especially

in the presence of females. Granny, Sonny's mother, is not in the office

or even the f'n wouldn't have been tolerated. Yesterday was Sonny's

65th birthday. There was a cake and for the first time trays of veggies

replaced the chips and creamy garlic dip. Sonny's father, the original Sonny,

had dropped like a lead puck at 62. Granny, his widow, now 92, lean as a whippet,

sharp as a tack, comes in every day to do the accounts. McGinty, part car salesman,

part-time pro hockey scout and thirty pounds lighter than when he retired

as the high school principal gnaws on a nub of left-over broccoli and agrees

it was a bit brutal. Taylor and Granny come in from the pumps trailed by Mickey,

aka the Owl, Packet photographer. *Great shot Champ* says McGinty.

Yeah chimes in Granny *reminds me why I don't take my hockey - playing*

great granddaughters to watch those games.

Peter Markus

Return of the Dogman

for John Rybicki

I am skating backwards
over your bones

here in this assembly line city
where we lose

our fingers and toes
to ice and snow and cars,

what little scrap is left
of our junk heap jalopy bodies

shaped by factories and rinks
we left but can never leave behind.

I am dragging you back
down the boarded up boulevard

where we will breathe
where we will drive through

the red dust boneyard
of Olympia's bulldozed bricks.

Brother, I want the two of us
to face off,

to stand nose to nose,
stick to stick,

on the front steps
of Joe Louis Arena,

street brawling boxers,
back alley dogs

snarling a little too much
like Ted Lindsay,

hungry for the heavens
to drop the puck.

Bill Templeman

They Don't Play Hockey Here Any More: The Montreal Forum's Chief Ghost Meditates Upon the History of the Game

I

They've taken out the boards, auctioned off the seats.
No one plays hockey anymore. Never mind.

Today I hate hockey! Let me be clear about this;
I really hate this farce they call hockey. I hate all that it stands for.

It used to be a game of skill and grace when the Rocket played
along with Geoffrion and Bouchard. Now it is a game of thugs.

Fast thugs, mind you, and strong like hell and big like moose
but stupid. The finesse is gone. It is now a big man's game.

Football is a big man's game. It is what the crowd wants.
The Americans, all they understand is the fights.

They want the WWF to impregnate the NFL
and have the progeny born live at centre ice on skates.

Football is a rich man's game. At least there is power,
there is strategy and there is courage in the execution.

Hockey has none of this anymore. It is all clutch and grab,
concussion and checking from behind, lawyers and endorsements.

Just watch. They bring the puck up to the blue line, dump it
into the corner then beat the shit out of the other guy,

as they try to bat it out into the slot where 9 times out of 10
it is cleared back to centre ice and the whole shebang starts all over.

Call that hockey? I call that bullshit. Yeah, they're fast alright.
And the bastards are rich like hell for taking part in this charade.

Me, I used wait for those electric nights in late March during the playoffs
(the playoffs used to wind up when they should, during the first April thaw)

when Harvey would feed the puck ahead to the Rocket who would
skate through the entire Red Wing team and terrorize Sawchuk

with a shot that would just about take off his ear.
The red light would flash on and the Forum would go wild.

Now the season goes too long. The finals end within pissing distance of July.
Who care about hockey in July? The old Forum would be too hot.

In those days all the boys would be lining up summer jobs beginning in April.
That's right. Even the Rocket had a summer job.

These days those thugs don't need summer jobs.
They golf with their accountants all summer.

II

The Rocket had to sell hair tonic after he retired.
Now those young thugs earn more in one year than he did in his whole life.

And they all speak crazy languages. It's bad enough that the Rocket had to learn
English to speak to his coach.

Now you have to speak Russian to your centre
and Swede to your defense.

Richard, he grew up in St Henri. There they only spoke French.
As an Habitant ghost, I tolerate the English, we need their bucks

but all the rest can just plain bugger off. This is our game, goddamnit.
Leave it alone.

The TV commercials were the beginning of the end.
Delays the game. Gotta keep them sponsors happy. Then came the Expansion.

Now they have more teams in cities with palm trees than they
have in cities with snow. Call that progress? Horseshit.

Ghosts aren't allowed into of their fancy pension plan.
Too old, they say. Played too long ago, they say.

So I haunt the old-timer's games at the smaller rinks.
I like the old rinks.

Some of the boys like Beliveau who got the smooth tongue

and know how to chat up the Molsons have done well.

Some, like Red Kelly and Frank Mahovalich

even made it to the Senate. That's good.

We need more people in high places who remember

how great the game used to be.

Anyway, thanks to the good people at Kellogg's, the Rocket is now at

your breakfast table every morning on your Corn Flakes box.

I hate the taste of the crap myself, but if it is good enough for Maurice Richard

it's good enough for me. A ghost doesn't eat much anyway.

I'll never make it to a Corn Flakes box and I'll never sit in the Senate.

You'll never catch me haunting that ritzy new rink downtown.

The old Forum is gone.

The locker room with John McCrae words painted on the wall

"To you from failing hands we throw
the torch; be yours to hold it high"

may soon be a video arcade. Even the old tavern is gone.

They don't play hockey here anymore

so I'll just hang out here in the rafters

and play crib with Howie Morenz and Toe.

After all, I've still got the best memories in the house.

Patricia McGoldrick Goldberg

Growing Up with Hockey

Growing up in rural southwestern Ontario, Canada, in the 1960s meant that hockey was an important part of my life.

From late autumn to spring, hockey was the topic of conversation for many Canadians at home, at work and at school. On the black and yellow school bus, we talked about the latest trades and standings and whether or not the coach should have taken out the goalie in a last ditch effort to gain a winning goal. Many of my friends played league hockey and we spent countless hours in cold arenas cheering our classmates on to victory.

Hockey was everywhere! Scott Young's *Scrubs on Skates* was a page turner for young hockey fans, girls and boys alike. An avid fan for many years, I kept a scrapbook dedicated to Frank Mahovlich – the Big M was the best! I treasured the articles about how the smooth skating player from northern Ontario had outdone Bobby Hull, the Golden Jet, by winning the Calder Cup for National Hockey League Rookie of the Year. Years later, I distinctly remember the tears that I shed on hearing the news that the Toronto Maple Leafs had traded my favorite player – to Detroit, of all places!

Before players' cards were sought for their market value, my brothers collected the Original Six and traded them with their friends. My sister and I had a collection of hockey coins to match their cards, in the hundreds. After telephone conferencing with my siblings, the *possible* source of these coins is believed to be numerous Jell-O boxes purchased over the weeks. Regardless of their point of origin, these colorful plastic and metal coins were a great substitute for game chips. We spent many hours doling out the precious coins as we played rummoli.

Hockey was more than a spectator sport. Each year, as soon as the water froze in our neighbor's pond, my brothers headed for the ice. Last year's skates were passed down from one to the other and at least one lucky person would be the fortunate recipient of a new "second-hand" pair of skates. My sister and I tagged along to the outdoor rink, hoping to get a chance to skate around before the big game began. Often, we were recruited for net-minding as well, depending on the turnout of players.

Only the coolest and crispest days of winter produced the best ice conditions for my brothers and their friends from neighboring farms. Once we arrived at the pond, shovels slid across the ice in record time. Markers for the goaltending nets were quickly procured from the snow-covered willows and before you knew it, hockey night (afternoon?) in Canada was underway.

Aspiring NHL stars passed the puck with timely teamwork. Crisp, "cannonading" slapshots (as Danny Gallivan would say) inspired by the style of Mahovlich, Gordie Howe and Jean Beliveau were fired towards the net with great intensity. The action was fast and furious, lacking only the voice of Foster Hewitt to announce the plays.

Time flew by, along with the forward passes. An hour elapsed and then another went by before the January cold started to pierce through the odd assortment of blue/white patched and mended hockey equipment. The frozen black rubber puck was retrieved and worn skates were exchanged for ice cold winter boots. The final score was tallied – Leafs 3/the Others 2. Shots on goal? Anybody's guess. Weary but happy, we waved good-bye to our friends for another week.

With skate blades wiped clean until next Sunday afternoon, we headed home to the warmth of the kitchen stove, a cup of hot chocolate, and a fast-paced game of rummoli, played with – you guessed it – hockey coins from our nation's best!

Diane Weber

Ice Dreams

for those who came before

At midnight, at two and at three,
black north country nights
in black north country winter,

long ago girls
race down the ice, screaming,
tasting deep the chilled air,

gliding along on the cold edge
of danger, gasping
for breath, fingertips beating

the pulse of the heart, slamming
the boards, feet flying
out, sliding along on the blade

of the ice, melting skin into ice,
swallowing hard a mouth full of plastic,
protecting against the curved stick,

the black disk of fury flying...
Nights on the ice, fought for
and embraced, by long ago girls,

skating and weaving, creating a team
of women playing hockey –
women plotting anarchy

Steven Shikaze

Hockey Dreams

The father takes his usual place in the stands. He checks his watch – quarter to seven; fifteen minutes to game time. He sits alone – away from the crowd of other parents with their cowbells, horns and other homemade noisemakers, away from their shrieks at the referee, the coach or the players. If things had turned out differently, he thinks, he might be among them; more likely, he'd be behind the bench, coaching.

The son sits in the corner of the dressing room listening intently to his coach, his eyes focused on a spot on the floor as he hears the lineup announced. As usual, he will be playing on the wing, on the second line. Having tied their son's skates and patted them on their helmets, the fathers have left the dressing room. The son listens to last-minute instructions – keep your stick on the ice and play your position. The son doesn't think about scoring goals for this or any other game – this is his second year of house league and he hasn't scored a goal yet. In his mind, however, he dreams of improving every year, and making the NHL. His skates are tight, his stick taped. He wants to win, but more than winning, he wants to play.

The atmosphere of a hockey arena on a cold February morning is like none other. The echo of coaches yelling; the sound of skate blades carving into the ice; the resounding pop of pucks hitting sticks as players practice slapshots. The dim, soft arena light; the aroma of Zamboni fumes, sweat and coffee, this is an atmosphere that triggers such vivid memories of the father's own childhood that he doesn't know whether to smile or cry. He had played competitive hockey until he was 13. Always excelling at every level of competition, he wore the captain's ÔC' for his last three seasons. The father has been watching his son play for nearly two seasons and the memories never fail to arise whenever he enters the rink, despite his desperate attempts to forget them.

. . .

6:55 AM. The players are skating around in the warm-up. The father sees number seventeen skating among bigger, better kids; kids whose parents cheer them on from the stands. The father sees his son consciously practicing his crossovers during the warm-up. Some teammates warm up the goalie by taking wrist shots from 20 feet away; others are practicing their stops and starts. Number seventeen calmly, yet diligently skates around the rink, seemingly oblivious to everything going on around him.

The son only started playing organized hockey last season at the age of ten. Because of his late start, other kids his age had a head start; most of his teammates have been playing since they were six or seven. After a very trying first season, the son forgot about hockey over the summer. With the arrival of fall, however, he felt the urge to sign up again, despite the hardship in his first year. Now here he is, near the end of his second year. He sees his father sitting alone at the far end of the stands. He acknowledges by lifting his stick in his father's direction. His father waves back furtively. The son has often asked him if he ever played organized hockey. The father always answers by saying he plays after work on Fridays with his friends from work, deftly avoiding the conversation by changing the subject to the son's game.

The last competitive hockey game the father played was more than two decades ago; he was thirteen and his own father was the coach of the team. His last game was the team's final preparation before a big tournament in Quebec. They lost that game; the coach singled him out. Embarrassed him in front of his teammates. Frustrated after years of trying to live up to his father's dreams, he quit the team. The coach, his father, would go to the tournament without his best player, the captain, his son.

For the father, the fun had left two or three years earlier. Once his own father realized the exceptional talent his boy had for the game, he pushed him harder. Driven by his own dreams, his father enrolled him in summer hockey camps and power skating lessons. The backyard was flooded in winter so he could practice skating and stickhandling. From house leagues to all-star teams to AA to AAA – at each level, he excelled. The further he moved up the ranks, however, the less passion he had for the game. Practices were three times a week, games anywhere from two to four. Weekends were spent traveling to tournaments. While his best friends remained at the house-league level, he was on the ice four times a week, with little time for anything else. The final straw was when his father decided to coach his team.

. . .

7:00 AM. The game begins, the son stands at the end of the players' bench watching the game, eager for his first shift. In three minutes, a buzzer will sound, and his shift will begin. The father watches the game with passing interest; one eye on the game and one eye on his son.

The second shift begins. The father sees his son and knows the minimal instructions the coach gave his son before the game. The son doesn't move any more than 10 feet from the boards and his stick is on the ice as if it was made of lead. When the puck comes to him, he swats at it, hitting it towards the opposition end, and skates after it with the enthusiasm of a puppy chasing after a tennis ball.

The game enters its final minutes with the score tied 1-1. The son is on the ice for the final shift. With seconds left on the clock, there is a scramble in front of the opposition's goal. The puck bounces towards the son who swats at it. He misses most of the puck but gets enough of it to knock it towards the net. The goalie smothers the puck and the final buzzer sounds. No overtime, no shootout. A tie.

During the drive home, the son is glowing. Did you see my shot? I almost scored! We would have won the game! I saw it, the father replies. He, too, is glowing; his dream fulfilled.

Richard Harrison

Coach's Corner

The almost clerical collar, he is the priest of rock 'em
sock 'em. He silences his more knowledgeable friends
with his faith in the bodies of men and without him
and his kind the NHL would be vapid as the All-Star
Game forever. He is loud and whiny and complaining
and chokes up on air if he's hurt by someone's words –
everything a man should not be, yet every sports bar
wills itself to quiet, turns up the volume on its dozen
sets only for his words. He is their man in a way no
hero of the play could be; his big league career was a
single game, but remember, he used to tell Bobby Orr
what to do and Bobby listened as we listen though we
let the game go on in silence. He slams foreigners,
praises women in all the ways wrong for our time,
rejects any wavering in the masculinity of his troops
like a colonel in the US Marines. And yet he is here
because he is unafraid to love, love the game, the
journeyman players, love the code that makes a man a
man and if you don't know, I ain't gonna tell ya. He
loves the fans, for all the pain they cause him, and we
are here with our own uncomfortable backs for that
dogged love, the voice that rises like a tenor sax,
pointed fingers, eyes narrowed to see clear and deep
the world that has him trapped on two sides already.

James R. Janz

The Beatific Vision Or, a Two on One

for Derek Faye and the
rest of the Vancouver Cyclones

If "perfect blessedness" is "a vision of God"
    as the late-reforming St Thomas Aquinas wrote
I've seen him
    or her
as recently as last Monday night
    at a beer-league hockey game played at Riley Park

You see, I put the puck around the boards to my partner
    he was waiting behind the net for it
        like he always does
and broke up the ice

He put it on the stick of the left-winger
    who for once was on the boards like he's supposed to be
        instead of turning lovely circles at the redline
        like he's in the goddamn Ice Capades
while the centre
    who's twenty pounds overweight, okay maybe thirty
hit the blueline in full stride just as the puck arrived

Our right-winger musta had his butt stapled to the boards
        but it didn't matter
    cus slicker'n "Slick 50" we were two on one

Their defenceman forced our centre wide
    playing the shot
but a smooth pass on my tape put me in cold
    the goalie came out to cut the angle
just as I slid a goalmouth pass back to the centre
    for the easy tap in

You see, you play a whole season for a moment like that
    maybe more
you endure broken bones
        and teeth
    dislocated shoulders
        torn-up knees
    souldeep bruises that take on kaleidoscope colours
                in the months they take to heal
and the numbing humiliation of playing a child's game
    with a rapidly aging body
less well than you did as a child

Yet we play
    and play
for just one more vision of perfect blessedness
    shared in silent communion

Gerald Hill

One Night Poems Fell

from the pressbox of Northlands Coliseum
to the ice surface. One of the linesmen,
true to his name, read
the lines, blew his whistle,
signalled with his arms.

One poem settled in the penalty box,
stayed there for the rest of the game,
wouldn't come out, an innocent poem
that never did anything wrong.

A poem slipped under the door
of the Oilers' dressing room,
sucked an orange with the boys.
Pinned up next to the photo
of the '84 champions the poem
terrifies visiting teams
who fear tradition and what
the poem might mean.

One of the wilder poems
deflected off the glass
into the crowd, cut
the side of a young boy's head.
He cried. They gave him
the poem as a souvenir.

A few of the harder poems
scored on Curtis Joseph
high to the glove side.
Joseph read them
disgustedly, squirted
his face with Gatorade, spat.

One poem jostled the opposition goon
who swore, dropped his gloves
but refused to read.
His mother never wanted to raise a goon,
can't bear to watch him get hurt.
She'd love to see her boy
in the corner with a poem.

A couple of poems were sucked outside
and settled on Gretzky's statue.
He carries not the Stanley Cup but poems
above his head. You can trade the man
but the poems stay.

A poem slipped into
one of the coach's notebooks.
When he spoke to his players
they skated so freely up the wing,
passed gently but hit hard.

A single poem
fell to centre ice, face up,
froze there. When the players
face off they struggle for possession
of a tiny black word.
Again and again they hunch
over to read.

Most of the poems
fell like inserts into programs. *What's this?* people said,
a poem? and they read until
the first intermission.

Is anything as silent
as 17,000 people reading poems?

Biographical Notes

Scott Beal teaches literature and writing at the University of Michigan, from which he received his MFA in 1996. He has had poems published in *Bellingham Review, Birmingham Poetry Review,* and *Alabama Literary Review.* His two cats are named Regan and Ophelia and behave accordingly.

Dorothea Belanger was born in Cooksville, Ontario. She lived in southern Ontario until the age of seven when her family moved to a fly-in Indian reserve in Northwestern Ontario where her father was a teacher. She obtained a degree in music from the University of Toronto and studied the flute extensively with Jeanne Baxtresser, former principal flutist of the New York Philharmonic. She has been featured in recital on CBC Radio's *Arts Encounter.* Presently Dorothea is interested in writing about creative and interpretive arts. She is a music teacher and lives in Kenora, Ontario with her husband and two sons.

Don Bell is a freelance writer and book scout who was born in Brooklyn, but lived most of his life in Montreal. He now divides his time between Sutton, in southern Quebec, and Paris. Author of the Leacock award winning book, *Saturday Night at the Bagel Shop,* and *Pocketman,* he is now finishing a book about the Montreal-connected death, in 1926, of magician Harry Houdini. In the late 1980's, he wrote a dozen or so offbeat, irreverent sports articles for the short-lived Canadian sports magazine, *MVP,* including "Hockey Night in Metabetchouan," which won a national magazine award in 1987.

David Bengtson lives in Long Prairie, Minnesota, where he has taught high school English for 30 years. He has received a Prize for Poetry from the Academy of American Poets and a Loft-McKnight Award for Creative Prose. His poems and short prose have appeared in a number of journals and anthologies, including *Ascent, Lake Country Journal, New Letters, New England Review, Northeast, 26 Minnesota Writers* (Nodin Press), and *The Sacred Place* (University of Utah Press). Two chapbooks of his writing have also been published, *The Man From Coal Lake* (Scythe Press) and *Open Windows* (Juniper Press). In the past few years, he has collaborated with his students and video artist Mike Hazard to produce a series of video poems based on his own poems. Some of these have been shown at The National Poetry Video Festival in Chicago and the National Poetry Association Cin(E)-Poetry Festival in San Francisco.

Adam Berlin received his MFA in Fiction Writing from Brooklyn College and teaches part time at John Jay College of Criminal Justice. His fiction and poetry have appeared in several literary magazines, most recently in *Other Voices, Santa Barbara Review, The Bilingual Review* (for which he was nominated for a 1997 Pushcart Prize*), The Dickinson Review, Puerto Del Sol,* and the sports literature magazines *Spitball* and *Aethlon*. He has recently completed a novel about boxing.

Lorna Blake lives and works in New York City, where she is Executive Director of the IOLA Fund, an organization that makes grants for civil legal services for the poor. She has poems forthcoming in *Pivot* and is currently working on a manuscript. The poem "Power Play" was written after not one, but many hockey games and is intended as an affectionate literary tribute to an intensely physical game.

Scott Boylston's short stories have appeared in *The Missouri Review, DoubleTake Magazine,* and *New Letters.* His short story "The Side Away from the Candle" was awarded the 1998 New Voice Fiction Award by the Writer's Voice in Manhattan. Scott spent his childhood playing hockey on the ponds, lakes, backyard rinks and indoor rinks of upstate New York. He and his wife, Kristin, have recently moved to Savannah, Georgia where he is a professor of graphic design at The Savannah College of Art & Design. He is presently working on a collection of short stories and has plans to begin serious work on a novel.

Tom Brand is a Midwestern writer, a native of International Falls, Minnesota, and a graduate of Wheaton College and the University of Minnesota, who spent and misspent his youth and maturity playing hockey on rinks in Indiana, Colorado, Wyoming, Illinois, and Minnesota. He teaches now at Bethel College in St. Paul. In addition to writing, he enjoys long-blade skating (ice and in-line). His goal for 1998 is to replace after many years the bridge that fills the gap a slapshot created in his smile during one of those wonderful times before face masks.

Although **Justin Bryant** grew up in Merritt Island, Florida, he has been a hockey fan for most of his 31 years. He recalls suffering through the early-80s domination of the New York Islanders (he was a Rangers fan). None of his friends – surfers! – cared. He has lived in London, Glasgow, Johannesburg, and the Florida Keys. Early writings were published in *The Iconoclast, Manna, Fan,* and *Florida Today.* In the last year he completed a novel loosely based on the 1994 free elections in South Africa. He is currently working on a novel of connected stories based on the fictitious Raleigh Flyboys featured in *Hakkanen's Move.* He now lives in Elon College, North Carolina, where he is completing the undergraduate degree in English he started 14 years ago.

Barry Butson is a Canadian who, in his other life, played hockey in the driveway, on the road, on the river, on the ponds, and in the arenas of southwestern Ontario. His Stratford team won many titles and included players like Nick Libett, Rick McCann and Hank Monteith, who all played for Detroit Red Wings eventually. Butson was minor athlete of the year once, but never made it as a pro hockey player. Instead, he went to university and became a writer and teacher. He could probably still put a few past a goalie, but spends his time writing poems that he hopes will bulge the net of people's consciousness in one way or another. About 200 of these poems have appeared in the literary magazines of Canada, the U.S.A., the U.K., France and Australia. His first collection, *East End Poems,* came out earlier in 1998. He is married, with three children, and has never been to Ireland or the Montreal Forum.

Nils Clausson lives and teaches in Regina, Saskatchewan. He is a poet and award-winning dramatist. His poem "Late Elegy Normandy Beach" was a runner-up this year in the National Poetry Contest Sponsored by the League of Canadian Poets, and will be published in *Vintage* 97/98. His poems have appeared in a wide range of journals, including *Madison Review, American Poets&Poetry, Tucumcari Literary Review, Phoenix, RE:AL, Thorny Locust, Blue Unicorn, Queer Poets Journal* and *modern words.* His one-act play, "Tess and the Boys," won first prize in the Second Annual Writing Contest sponsored by *Whetstone,* where it appeared in Spring 1997. He is president of Oscar Wilde & Company, a theatre company specializing in plays dealing with contemporary social and political issues.

Peter Desy is retired from the English Department of Ohio University. He has published in many literary magazines and anthologies and has two chapbooks and a full-length poetry collection (*Driving from Columbus*) from Edwin Mellen

Press, 1992. His father was owned by the Montreal Canadiens, played in the old league for Buffalo, Rhode Island, Fort Erie, and for two years with the Canadiens. Peter played hockey on the rivers and lakes when he was a kid, but later it got too hard to get enough guys to play indoor games, so he quit. Alas.

Clare Ferguson was born in England, but moved to Canada at the age of three. Growing up in Southern Ontario, hockey was always a big part of her life, from watching her brother play to attending Junior A games. Currently she resides with her husband and their four children and they continue the hockey tradition, often spending 4 or 5 nights at the arena. In her spare time Clare enjoys her position as Public Awareness Coordinator for the local Down Syndrome society and spends many hours on the internet researching resources for inclusion of people with special needs in school and community. This is her first published work.

While her son skates across New York and neighboring states, **Tina Lincer First** continues to sharpen her writing game. She is an award-winning essayist and fiction writer whose work has been published by *Writer's Digest,* the *Los Angeles Times Syndicate, The Women's Times,* the *Jewish Monthly,* the *Albany Times Union* and numerous other magazines and newspapers. She has worked as a dance critic, columnist, reporter and editor and currently serves as senior writer at a leading communications firm in upstate New York. She is the author of a screenplay, "Herschel," and is at work on a novel. A native of New York City, she lives in Loudonville, N.Y., with her two children and two cats. In between running to the rink, writing and raising kids, she also likes to paint, dance and garden.

Although **Patricia McGoldrick Goldberg** left her rural beginnings to attend the University of Guelph and to teach in urban areas, the memories of childhood days on the farm have stayed with her and have been the source of many poems and reflections. She has been published in *Wellington County History, The Kitchener Record, The Changing Image, Voices and Visions, The Grand Table Anthology, Cross Cultures,* and *Visual Verses.*

Beth Goobie is the author of twelve books as well as several plays. Her collection of poetry, *Scars of Light* (NeWest Press, Edmonton, 1994), won the Pat Lowther Memorial Award and is in reprint. Her latest novel for young adults, *The Colors of Carol Molev* (Roussan Publishers, Montreal, 1998) concerns hockey and the paranormal. Her latest novel for adults is *The Only Good Heart* (Pedlar Press, 1998). She has been shortlisted for the Governor General's Award for Children's Literature.

John Grey is an Australian born poet, playwright, musician, but has lived in the United States since the late seventies. He is a confirmed Bruins fan and hopes to see them lift Lord Stanley's Cup at least once before he passes on. He has been published in numerous literary journals, including *Wisconsin Review, Witness, Poet Lore, Green Mountains Review, Greensboro Review, New Delta Review, Texas Review,* and many others. His latest book is *Pointing The Gun* from Dark Regions Press. In addition, he has had plays produced in both New York City and Los Angeles and was three times voted best poet by the Genre Writer's Association for work in the Horror/ Science Fiction/Fantasy field.

Dan Hammond, Jr. resides in Arlington, Texas. His short stories have been published in *Fiction Quarterly, Pleiades, The Pinehurst Journal,* and *Southwestern American Literature.* He received a 1994 Umana Award for short fiction and was a 1996 semi-finalist for the American Fiction award. Last year he attended the Iowa Writers Workshop led by Frank

Conroy. Currently he is re-writing his first novel, *The Solomon Twist.* Mr. Hammond is employed by *The Dallas Morning News* as the Home Delivery Manager for their group of community newspapers surrounding Dallas. He graduated from Transylvania University in Lexington, Kentucky and acquired a Masters degree in Social Work from the University of Texas in Arlington. Mr. Hammond participates in a wide variety of sports but has never actually set foot on the ice. The idea for "For Next Year" came as he and his sons, Tyler and Travis, watched the finale of the Fort Worth Fire season in 1993.

Richard Harrison's 50 poems about hockey, *Hero of the Play,* is the only book of poetry ever given public reading at both The Hockey Hall of Fame in Toronto and at The Saddledome, home of the NHL Calgary Flames. Author of three books, Richard has read this work on several radio stations including Toronto's sports-only The FAN, and CBC's flagship *Morningside.* CBC's premiere arts program, *Adrienne Clarkson Presents,* aired a 40-minute TV documentary matching readings from the book with hockey footage from the 40s to the present. Of *Hero of the Play, Hockey Night in Canada's* Ron MacLean wrote, "If all the world's a stage, all of Canada is a rink. Richard Harrison un-ices the game which makes us feel as we do." Currently Richard teaches English and Creative Writing at Calgary's Mount Royal College.

Ronn Hartviksen learned to skate, as a boy, on outdoor rinks, often playing hockey on a nearby creek. Presently he and his family maintain a backyard rink known, affectionately, as the Bean Pot in Thunder Bay, Ontario. This year marks their nineteenth season. The rink is also a medium for outdoor ice painting, and, the seasonal postcards painted onto the ice have ranged from Christmas Greetings and Celtic calligraphy to the subject of whales, the New

Yorker's Eustace Tilley or even to a large portrait of *Hockey Night in Canada's* Don Cherry. Ronn's written work has appeared in the *Observer, Canadian Living, Magnetic North, Profile, Face Off, and Hope and Lake Superior Magazine.* He writes for a Northwestern Ontario publication called *Green Mantle.* At present he is in the midst of compiling a book, tentatively titled, *Hard To Get It Right,* a collection of travel, sports, and reflective pieces.

Hugh Hennedy, a graduate of Notre Dame, Columbia, and Boston universities, is a professor emeritus of the University of New England. He has published articles in scholarly journals on, among other writers, Chaucer, Shakespeare, and Austen. His book on Anthony Trollope's Barsetshire Novels, *Unity in Barsetshire,* was published by Mouton in 1971. His poetry has been published in many different journals, including *Tar River Poetry, Hawaii Review,* and *James Joyce Quarterly,* and it has been collected in *Old Winchester Hill* (Enright House, 1993) and *Halcyon Time* (Oyster River Press, 1993). He played hockey at Thayer Academy, in Braintree, Massachusetts, and in leagues in Lewiston, Portland, and Biddeford, Maine. He lives now in Portsmouth, New Hampshire, where occasionally he finds pick-up games to play in.

Long-time Toronto Maple Leaf fan **Gerald Hill** models his life and work after the great Leaf defenceman, Borje Salming. The hallmarks of Salming's play – creative flair on offence, gangly ruggedness on defence, intense team loyalty and courage, even a certain Nordic loneliness – are the hallmark's of Hill's play on a good day. In the off-season, Hill teaches English at Luther College at the University of Regina and parents two Leaf fans.

Anna A. Hillen crawled out of white-knuckle poverty in Toronto's inner city by jumping through every educational hoop placed in her path, then had her revenge by becoming a teacher herself, subverting the system regularly for the next thirty-three years. In June, 1992 she grabbed her pension and, salivating noticeably, leapt fearlessly into retirement. Now, like a kid at the midway, she tries her hand at everything: monthly columnist, free-lance writer, published poet, stand-up comic, church lector and resident culture vulture in a vibrant Ontario village of three thousand. Beats the hat trick 'though the pay's not as good.

Dale Jacobs teaches writing at East Carolina University in Greenville, North Carolina. He has published poems in *The MacGuffin, Main Street Rag Poetry Journal, South Dakota Review, Flint Hills Review, Thorny Locust, Pink Cadillac Review,* and *Fan Magazine.* His first book of poems, *Beneath the Horse's Eye,* was published in 1998 by Spotted Cow Press.

James R. Janz is an English instructor at Columbia College in Vancouver, BC, Canada. The downtown campus is a stone's throw away from GM Place, home of the Vancouver Canucks. James plays defense for the Vancouver Cyclones, where he cultivates a unique style, one cleverly designed to land him a leading role in any sequel to *Slap Shot.* Perhaps not surprisingly, he met his wife while he was in the penalty box and she was keeping the time keeper company. Reports that her continued presence in the time keeper's box that season led him to accumulate a team record penalty total remain unproven. His poetry has appeared in a number of Canadian publications including *Newest Review* and *Prairie Fire.* He is an assistant editor for *The Capilano Review.* He awaits the new beer league season with keen anticipation.

John B. Lee is a full-time writer living in Brantford, Ontario. With 23 published books to date, his work has been published internationally in over 200 magazines, periodicals, anthologies and literary journals. He has performed his poems and songs and read his work across Canada and the United States. He taught Creative Writing to Advanced Writers at Canadore College, was the Poet-in-Residence at the University of Windsor, participated in the Voices of the North Conference at the University of Maine and taught Creative Writing, Dramatic Arts and English at Waterford District High School from 1976-1989 with a one year interruption while he taught Science Fiction and Fantasy at the University of Western Ontario in 1983-4. He was born in 1951 and grew up on a farm in Highgate, near Chatham in Southwestern Ontario. He graduated from the University of Western Ontario with an Honours Degree in English (1974), a B. Ed. (1975), and a Master of Arts in Teaching English (1985). He plays hockey six times a week in the winter and once a week in summer, and he still isn't very good at it. His book of hockey poems, *The Hockey Player Sonnets,* was published by Penumbra Press in 1991.

Christine MacKinnon has been writing, literally, since she could hold a pencil. She is currently a reporter for the *Saugus (MA) Advertiser.* Christine writes a weekly column, "Off Deadline," in which this essay was first published. Though more a baseball than hockey fan, Christine was completely caught up in the Paralympic frenzy. "We're proud of Joey to the point of being obnoxious," she said. "But we thought, we're family, we're allowed." Christine's other work has appeared in *Cosmopolitan, Old Hickory Review, Grasslands Review,* and *Out of Words.* Her young adult manuscript, *Buckle the Toad,* is currently under consideration at Dutton Books. She lives in the Boston area and fervently hopes Fenway Park's Green Monster does not go the way of the Boston Garden parquet floor.

Peter Markus writes: "I'll never forget those days when my dad would wake me up at 4:30 in the morning to go to the rink, the ice misted over so thick it was like skating on a cloud, or floating across heaven. Poetry is as close as I can get to that feeling of breaking in all alone on the goaltender, the sound of the puck banging up against the back of the net. I live with my wife (who I met at a hockey game in my hometown of Trenton, Michigan) and our two children in Hockeytown–a.k.a. Motown, i.e. Detroit–and I write poems because I can no longer make a puck dance and sing. When the Red Wings won the Stanley Cup in '97, I spent the night dancing up and down Woodward Avenue with my friend, poet John Rybicki, to whom 'Return of the Dogman' is dedicated."

Peter McEwen is a teacher, artist, writer, grandfather and a hockey veteran who has been playing the game for more than half a century. As a poet, he is but a rookie. McEwen is working on his first collection of poems as well as a series of illustrated verse for children. In hockey, he has always relied on speed and skill. He is not a fan of violence, dislikes intensely the Don Cherry school of mayhem and is convinced that today's game is definitely in need of large ice surfaces; he also supports women's hockey. McEwen lives in Rugby, Ontario where one can still skate on the pond in the winter.

Thomas Michael McDade lives in Monroe, CT, with his wife Carol and works in Meriden, CT, as a computer programmer in the plumbing distribution field. He grew up in Pawtucket, RI, not far from the late Narragansett Park where Alsab once defeated Whirlaway, and played Boys' Club baseball in what is now the home of the Pawtucket Red Sox. He attended his first hockey game in 1962 (the RI Reds beat the Rochester Red Wings). After high school, he joined the Navy, serving on the USS Mullinnix and on shore at The Fleet Anti-Air Warfare Training Center in Virginia Beach. Following discharge he attended Fairfield University where he received a BA in English in 1973. He re-enlisted in the Navy in 1974 and made two Mediterranean cruises aboard the USS Miller. His work has appeared in many small press publications, as well as *Ted Williams: A Tribute* (Masters Press, 1997).

Joanne Merriam is a poet and arts administrator from the home of the Mooseheads: Halifax, Nova Scotia. She was educated at Dalhousie University and now works at the Writers' Federation of Nova Scotia. Her work has also appeared in such Canadian literary journals as *The Amethyst Review, The Antigonish Review, Feux chalins,* and *Grain.* She feels a nostalgic longing for the victories of childhood street hockey, and dreams of season tickets.

Ken O'Keefe is Canadian, born 1930, in Cornwall, Ontario. His roots are in the Ottawa and St. Lawrence Valleys where he grew in close contact with nature. A typical Canadian lad, he spent his youthful winters on outdoor hockey rinks, imitating Maurice "the Rocket" Richard, dreaming about Maple Leaf Gardens. Ken is a Basilian priest who devoted 25 years teaching high school English and Latin; since 1980 he has been engaged in campus ministry at the University of Western Ontario in London and at the University of Toronto. Gerald Manly Hopkins, Robert Frost and Walt Whitman are some poets who have influenced his writing.

A native of Cohoes, New York, **Gus Pelletier** holds B.A. and M.A. degrees in English from Siena College, and a Doctor of Arts in English degree from the State University of New York Center at Albany. He has served as an NEH residency fellow at UNC-Chapel Hill (1980-81), and as a visiting scholar at Yale (1982) and Cornell (1986). His published work has appeared in a variety of anthologies, journals, and reviews in the United States and Canada, most notably in the *Dalhousie*

Review, the *Maryland Review,* the *Kentucky Poetry Review,* and in the *Notre Dame Review.* Gus and his wife, Jane, are the parents of nine grown children, and they live in Bovina Center, a small, rural town in upstate New York.

Marion Rapp discovered hockey when she was in 9th grade. She used to stay up and listen to New York Ranger games when Harry Howell was a defenseman. She has lived in New Jersey all her life, and was a charter member of the New Jersey Devils Fan Club. She is married to Ken Rapp, who is not a sports fan. She has a son, Steve, and a daughter-in-law, Lori, both of whom enjoy the game, and hopes to indoctrinate her granddaughter, Emily Morgan. She has had various articles and stories published in children's and adult magazines, but except for a limerick in *Bass Line,* this is her first published poem.

Steven Shikaze was born in Toronto, Ontario, Canada, in the year before the Toronto Maple Leafs won their most-recent Stanley Cup. He grew up in the suburb of Scarborough and in Ottawa where, while skating on the Rideau or playing street hockey, he dreamed of playing in the NHL. He currently lives in Waterloo, Ontario where he works as a research scientist and consultant. He has recently started to write fiction in his spare time, and "Hockey Dreams" is his first short story about his favorite sport. An avid hockey fan and player, Steve longs for his beloved Maple Leafs to win the Stanley Cup.

Rob Siciliano is a Toronto-based spoken word performer/drummer/punk athlete/hockey nut. He put out a cassette in 1995 entitled *Heckler Night* and released his debut spoken word CD, *Flammable,* in 1996. Rob toured in support of the disc and has read his work in four countries. His follow-up CD is entitled *Fresh From The Espresso Machine* and he will hit the road once again, unleashing many a verbal assault. Rob is a devout Montreal Canadiens fan. He can be contacted at PO Box 1042, Station F, Toronto, Ontario, Canada M4Y 2T7 or batteringram@hotmail.com

Robin Springer grew up part of a large family in a tight-knit neighborhood in a small town in upstate New York. She currently lives in North Carolina, where ice hockey games are just a sweet memory. Robin attends East Carolina University, in Greenville, North Carolina, where she is pursuing a Masters Degree in English Education. She is also Elaine, Anna, and Meredith's mom, and partner to her husband Dave. "Pickup Hockey" is her first published essay.

Bill Templeman lives in Milton, Ontario where he is a Partner of Ascent Associates, an organizational management consulting firm. He has performed his poetry at numerous venues in the Toronto area.

Sue Ellen Thompson is the author of two books of poetry, *This Body of Silk* (Northeasten University Press, 1986) and *The Wedding Boat* (Owl Creek Press, 1995). In the summer of 1998 she was the Poet in Residence at the Frost Place in Franconia, New Hampshire. Some of her recent poems have appeared in *The Dominion Review, Laurel Review, Rosebud,* and *Tar River Poetry.* She is currently Visiting Writer at Central Connecticut State University.

Brian Turner works at Smith College. His fiction has appeared in *The Northwest Review, Weirdo,* and *VMag*; his cartoons have been published under his pseudonym, Renrut, in newspapers and magazines, most notably Z. He lives in Florence, Massachusetts.

Edo van Belkom's over 120 short stories have appeared in a wide variety of magazines and anthologies including *Year's Best Horror* and *Best American Erotica.* He is the author of three novels, *Wyrm Wolf, Lord Soth,* and *Mister Magick,* a short story collection, *Death Drives a Semi,* and a book of nonfiction entitled *Northern Dreamers.* Born in Toronto in 1962, he worked as a sports reporter before becoming a full-time freelance writer in 1992. He currently lives in Brampton, Ontario with his wife Roberta and son Luke. His home page is located at www.horrornet.com/belkom.htm

Bob Wakulich is currently working on his Masters Degree in Creative Writing at the University of British Columbia. He has published prose and poetry in a number of Canadian and American journals and anthologies. He is currently putting together a collection of his poetry, tentatively called *The Questionable Part of Town.* He plans to buy a nice pair of dress shoes some time in the coming year.

Diane Weber graduated cum laude from St. Lawrence University with a BS in Biology and English, and has worked toward her MA in English at Iona College. She is Public Relations Officer for Ramapough Poets. In addition to her role in Ramapough Poets, she is Research Editor and columnist for *Poetic Voices*, a monthly online magazine. Her poetry has appeared in national small press publications and web-zines, such as *Plainsongs* and *Poetry Heaven.* She is completing *White Crow,* a manuscript of poetry. While an undergraduate, Diane was a founding member of St. Lawrence University's women's ice hockey program.

Acknowledgements

Some of the works in this collection appeared previously in the following journals and books. They are as follows:

"Hockey Night in Métabetchouan" by Don Bell first appeared in *MVP.*

"A Drink" by David Bengtson first appeared in his chapbook *Open Windows* (Juniper Press).

"Captains by Default" by Scott Boylston first appeared in *The Missouri Review.*

"My Father's Picture On The Cover Of a Buffalo Bison's Hockey Program For 1934" by Peter Desy has appeared in *Poetry East* and in his book *Driving from Columbus* (Edwin Mellon Press).

"For Next Year" by Dan Hammond, Jr. first appeared in *Southwestern American Literature.*

"Using the Body," "Stanley Cup," and "Coach's Corner" by Richard Harrison first appeared in his book *Hero of the Play* (Wolsak and Wynn Publishers).

"Of Ice & Men" by Ronn Hartviksen first appeared in *Canadian Living.*

"The Middle of America" and "Shinny" by Dale Jacobs first appeared in *Beneath the Horse's Eye* (Spotted Cow Press).

"The Beatific Vision Or, a Two on One" by James R. Janz first appeared in *NeWest Review.*

"Hockey Heart," "Last Night it Snowed," and "The Firehall Blues" by John B. Lee first appeared in his book *The Hockey Player Sonnets* (Penumbra Press).

"Bladed Grace" by Christine MacKinnon first appeared in the *Saugus (MA) Advertizer.*

"In the Heat of Gratitude" by Gus Pelletier first appeared in *The Baltimore Review.*